Improve your Child's IQ and Behaviour

IMPROVE YOUR CHILD'S

IQ
AND

BEHAVIOUR

DR. STEPHEN SCHOENTHALER

Foreword by
Hans J. Eysenck

BBC BOOKS

Published by BBC Books,
a division of BBC Enterprises Limited,
Woodlands, 80 Wood Lane, London W12 0TT

First published 1991

© Stephen Schoenthaler 1991

Foreword © Hans J. Eysenck

ISBN 0 563 36193 X

Graphs and Tables by
Graham Dudley Associates

Set in Linotron Plantin by
Phoenix Photosetting Ltd, Chatham, Kent
Printed and bound in England by Clays Ltd, St Ives plc
Cover printed by Clays Ltd, St Ives plc

Contents

Acknowledgements

The research that went into this book has taken me ten years to complete. Neither the research nor the book would have been completed without the support of many people. John Wacker, President of the Wacker Foundation, provided me with the necessary funds to do most of the work before 1986. When certain medical and food industry representatives denounced my work and ridiculed the findings, my colleagues in my department, particularly Professor Walter Doraz and Stephen Amos, stood by me, deflected the attacks, and encouraged me to persevere. Without the support of my peers at California State University Stanislaus, I would have taken a non-controversial course by doing research in areas that did not offend any special interest groups.

I owe a debt of gratitude to the Oklahoma Department of Health and Human Services which was the first state agency to realise that my work had to be taken seriously, and subsequently allowed me to conduct the first properly controlled trial on intelligence, crime, and nutrition.

I would like to thank the British Broadcasting Corporation, and their producer Tony Edwards, who has followed my research since 1983. In 1987, he produced 'Your Child's Diet on Trial' (shown on QED in January 1988) which reported the unfolding of the first controlled trial in this field.

Without Tony Edwards' and the BBC's interest, I believe my work would have been largely ignored, because if the truth is known, my research has only confirmed what others have already speculated to be true. The national coverage not only brought the issue to the forefront where it belongs, but generated the fiscal support to conduct a definitive trial of whether nutrition can affect intelligence. I owe a debt of thanks to the Dietary Research Foundation and its Chairman of the Board of Trustees, Graham Aaronson, for funding my research and believing in its importance.

I should like to thank Suzanne Scott for help with the manuscript.

Most of all, though, I am indebted to my wife Mary, who has lived with my research and all its vicissitudes over the years. She has endured the anguish and frustration when projects have gone awry, when ideas have proved false, when my confidence has waned, and has done so with a reservoir of support and love. When we had no funds to back the experiments, Mary willingly worked to raise the money I needed. No words can adequately thank her. I dedicate this book to Mary.

Stephen Schoenthaler

About the Author

Dr Stephen Schoenthaler, an American Professor of Criminology, is one of the world's leading authorities on the effects of nutrition on behaviour and intelligence. He has pioneered the research on the subject, with studies on 3000 juvenile delinquents and over a million schoolchildren.

Foreword

There is a saying in Germany: 'Man ist was man isst' – 'one is what one eats'. Of course this is not true in the broad sense; what we are is determined by genetics and by events that happen to us, of which the food we eat is only one, and perhaps not the most important. Nevertheless, there is an ancient tradition linking intelligence to what we eat – fish nourishes the brain, oysters feed our virility, roast beef and Yorkshire pudding make John Bull what he is. Scientists have been more cautious in their views; large studies such as the Dutch starvation study in 1972 found no evidence that severe undernourishment in early childhood was detrimental when intelligence was measured at induction into the army, and the undernourished compared with properly nourished controls.

But perhaps it is not the total amount eaten, measured in calories consumed, that is important, but the *kind* of food consumed. In particular, certain vitamins and minerals are needed for proper growth and good physical health – perhaps something similar applies to mental health, intelligence and socialised behaviour. As early as 1955, Harrell, Woodyard and Gates published a monograph, 'The effects of mothers' diets on the intelligence of offspring', which showed that when in New York women of low socio-economic status were given vitamin and mineral supplements during pregnancy, their children at 4 years of age averaged 8 points higher in IQ than a control group of children whose mothers were given placebos during pregnancy. Alas, the *Zeitgeist* was hostile to the idea of intelligence as a largely biological entity, determined by the physical action of the cortex, and there was little follow-up. A few studies were reported, largely supporting the view that mineral and vitamin supplementation can raise IQ in children deficient in these particulars, but these aroused little interest in a public more concerned with Headstart and other attempts (nearly all of them abortive) to raise IQ through better education.

In January 1988 BBC Television's *QED* transmitted a programme called 'Your Child's Diet on Trial'. The programme reported on the findings of two scientific trials examining the nutrition of adolescents, both of which were completed three months earlier, and came to the same remarkable conclusions.

First, a study by Californian Professor of Criminology, Dr Stephen Schoenthaler: this showed that giving juvenile delinquents vitamin and mineral supplements significantly decreased their anti-social behaviour and increased their IQ. Second, a British experiment by psychologist Dr David Benton and science master Gwilym Roberts; they too reported on *QED* that supplements appeared to increase schoolchildren's IQ.

'Your Child's Diet on Trial' also claimed that some children in Britain are significantly malnourished, and implied that, if these new findings were true, their poor diets might be adversely affecting their behaviour and academic performance.

The effect of the programme was sensational. The next day pharmacies, health-food stores and supermarkets found their shelves emptied of vitamin pills, as the British public rushed out to buy supplements for their children. Newspapers ran scores of features based on the programme; some of the articles were critical, quoting a number of expert nutritionists who said that the programme's conclusions were unjustified. They said that children's diets in Britain were quite good, and that nobody really needed supplements. They also pooh-poohed the whole notion that IQ and behaviour might be adversely affected by a poor diet.

In fact, although the general public was fascinated by the startling new findings suggesting a hitherto unrecognised effect of nutrition on teenage behaviour and IQ, both academia and government almost entirely ignored them.

And yet, however controversial its conclusions, the programme might have been expected to be of more than passing interest to nutritional experts in at least two government departments. After all, it isn't as if Britain leads the world in educational achievement or civilised behaviour. Juvenile crime and hooliganism are on the increase, and the Home Office appears unable to halt it; likewise the decline in educational achievement seems to be immune to the best efforts of the Department of Education and Science. Neither of these bodies appeared to take the slightest notice of the programme.

However, the programme did stir a handful of people to act: a community-health group of scientists acquired the funds to mount a repeat trial in a school in Dundee; top nutritionist Professor Donald Naismith was moved to do a similar study in London; and a number of vitamin manufacturers approached David Benton with offers to help continue his research.

But the most significant spin-off from the programme came not from within academia or commerce, but from a private charitable foundation owned by Graham Aaronson QC, a leading financial lawyer in London. He considered the IQ and behaviour/nutrition debate opened up by *QED* so important that he was prepared to back further studies – to the tune of over half a million pounds. He asked Dr Stephen Schoenthaler to carry out most of the research.

(The story of the new discoveries since January 1988 forms the basis of a second *QED* programme – scheduled for transmission in February 1991 – much of which concerns the work of Stephen Schoenthaler.)

The 1988 *QED* brought Stephen Schoenthaler's work to the notice of the general public, and also of many academics who had not read his earlier articles, buried in little-known journals and magazines. His earliest work had been poorly controlled, but his Oklahoma study showed that juvenile criminals who had taken supplements decreased their violent behaviour overall by 40%, in properly controlled double-blind experiments. He also found, in other studies, large effects of dietary improvements in increasing IQ.

And yet Stephen's findings were still ignored. Moreover, he was accused of doing research to promote the taking of vitamin supplements, rather than recommending people to improve their diet – somewhat ironical when for the previous ten years he had done nothing but that.

Nevertheless, some scientists did not have entirely closed minds. In particular, the leading nutritionist Professor John Yudkin, although initially extremely sceptical, took the trouble to look at Stephen's data in detail – and came away convinced that here was a profoundly important set of findings. I, too, started out a sceptic, but was impressed by the rigour of the work, its extent, and the very positive results. Linus Pauling, already convinced by his own work, agreed to join us on the scientific directorate which was to supervise the work and guarantee its objectivity; also involved was Professor Eric Peritz, a well-known statistician.

Stephen Schoenthaler must now rank as probably the world's leading authority on the effects of nutrition on anti-social behaviour and intelligence. Without him this field would have remained wholly undeveloped. Over the past fifteen years, in the teeth of considerable academic hostility, he and his research team have taken the subject from a 'fringe' topic into a new and exciting area of science with an impressive body of data.

So it is fitting that he should write a book in order to tell the story of his pioneering research, and summarise the latest findings. For the professional scientist, psychologist and nutritionist, the book will be a unique review of the research data; for the layman, it will be a source of valuable practical advice on nutrition for themselves and their family.

Hans J. Eysenck, Ph.D., D.Sc.,
Professor Emeritus of Psychology,
University of London

1 Food, IQ and Behaviour

Most books begin at the beginning; but because the conclusion of this book is so important, I'm going to begin at the end.

My main conclusion is very simple: if you want to improve children's IQ and behaviour, one of the ways is to give them nutritious food.

So if you're flicking through this book wondering whether to buy it, and you're feeling hard up, save your money. Put the book back on the shelf, go home and make sure your children don't eat junk. That way they'll stand a better chance of not becoming delinquents, and they'll probably get higher marks at school. The same applies to any of you who are about to become mothers: eat as well as you can, and your baby will be brighter and better behaved.

Also, if you want to improve your child's IQ and behaviour, but you don't know enough about nutrition, or you can't afford to eat well, or your child absolutely refuses to eat anything but junk, a good vitamin and mineral pill taken every day is an acceptable second-best alternative.

Now, this all sounds pretty sensible, perhaps even obvious, but I doubt whether you will find this advice in many other books. Because the fact is that, until very recently, it wasn't at all obvious that bad eating habits can affect how you think and behave. Indeed, even today, most experts consider the whole idea stuff and nonsense.

For example, you won't find many experts in crime – like probation officers, judges, prison governors, psychiatrists or policemen – who believe that giving juvenile delinquents a vitamin pill might make some of them less violent. In the field of education, very few experts have ever said good nutrition will help pupils do better at school. And as for experts in nutrition itself, they cannot see how there can be any possible connections between a child's diet, and its IQ and behaviour.

To be frank, a few years ago, neither could I. In fact it has taken me ten years to convince myself that the connection is real: ten years of research involving over 8000 juvenile delinquents, and over a million schoolchildren; ten years of step-by-step discoveries that slowly built up like clues in a detective story. And because what I was discovering was so opposed by the experts, it had to be a painstaking and thorough investigation, so that I could be a hundred per cent certain of my conclusions.

Food and Crime

Although today my reputation is in the field of nutrition, my background is in crime. Fifteen years ago, in 1975, I had just completed my master's degree in sociology with a specialisation in deviant behaviour, at Syracuse University in New York. While teaching at a local community college in upstate New York, I was given the opportunity to teach inside Attica Correctional Facility. Four years before, the bloodiest and deadliest prison riot in history had occurred at this institution and shocked the world. Thirty-eight men died, many of whom were prison inmates. Working there had a profound impact upon me. I often found myself alone with groups of twenty to thirty inmates, most of whom were serving sentences ranging from twenty-five years to life for murder, first-degree manslaughter, or rape.

A year later, I began studying for a PhD at the State University of New York partly because certain experiences at Attica haunted me. While I was convinced that the authorities were making every conceivable effort to provide meaningful treatment programmes for the inmates, environment fostered hatred, which preven rehabilitation. To my mind, there had to be a bette control crime.

I was young and idealistic, but as my studies of criminology deepened I became faced with the depressing fact that very few measures to rehabilitate criminals actually seemed to work. Indeed, out of over 250 kinds of rehabilitation programmes tried in US prisons since 1945, only nineteen have shown any signs of working at all. And yet I felt sure that there had to be a way, there had to be something we could do to help criminals, and hopefully prevent crime as well. The tough part was finding a scheme that was practical, cost-effective, and humane – and above all one that actually worked.

It was pure coincidence that first put me on the track of a possible solution, which has become my life's work ever since.

When I was awarded my PhD in 1980, I happened to be teaching undergraduates at a college in Virginia. By chance, one of the local juvenile detention facilities (in Britain the equivalent would be a juvenile remand centre) was run by a remarkable man by the name of Frank Kern. Frank was one of those rare people in the prison system – an idealist with a mind of his own. He was also something of a health freak, and he believed passionately that crime, and particularly juvenile crime, was caused by – wait for it – sugar.

To me the idea that sugar was responsible for delinquency was laughable. But I hid my scepticism behind a polite smile, and listened.

Frank told me that the sugar and crime idea had originally come from two US researchers, Alexander Schauss and Barbara Reed. They had each independently come to the conclusion that excessive sugar consumption caused a medical condition called reactive hypoglycaemia which in turn affected people's behaviour so much that they became

Food, IQ and Behaviour 3
I knew that the
gested effective way to

...emia?

...lled glucose, is what powers the
...down by the body to make glucose,
...des a steady and gradual trickle of
...ream for several hours.

.., all forms of sugar tend to be absorbed
...es. When a meal, high in sugar, is eaten on
..., blood sugar rises quickly and often reaches
u........s of the normal range (between 90 and 110
millig...   .r decilitre).

The pan.reas responds to the rise in blood sugar by releasing
insulin into the blood stream. The released insulin helps cells
pull the excessive glucose out of the blood. The glucose is then
stored in the liver and muscle tissue as glycogen. This causes the
sugar concentrations in the blood to decrease. The pancreas
releases even more insulin as the blood sugar rises. When foods
high in sugar raise the level of blood sugar too far, too much
insulin can be released. The excess insulin causes too much
glucose to be pulled out of the blood and makes the blood sugar
level too low. This is how a high-sugar diet can lower blood sugar
shortly after a meal. The theory is that because the glucose levels
are low, the cells' fuel is depleted, and the first cells to be affected
are those in the brain. Brain waves, which are electrical
impulses, change when glucose or oxygen falls too low. These
impulse changes are more marked in the frontal region of the
brain where thought and reasoning is believed to occur. This
region requires five time as much energy as the central part of
the brain known as the limbic system. According to a current,
popular hypothesis among brain researchers, the frontal lobes
are responsible for controlling and shaping our emotions, which
are largely the products of our limbic system.

People with lowered energy production are likely to feel
tension, depression, anger, fatigue and/or confusion. Thought
becomes more difficult, and attending to a task becomes almost
impossible. Impulsive behaviour is likely to increase and
sometimes it can be violent.

violent. And the reason people were eating too much sugar was because of their increasing consumption of so-called 'junk food'.

Barbara Reed was a senior probation officer in Ohio, and had for the previous few years been claiming what sounded like fantastic success in rehabilitating young offenders, simply by keeping them off junk food and putting them on a low-sugar diet. In fact in 1977 she had been asked to testify before the US Senate about her work, and she told them that in over 250 cases 'we have not had one single person back in court who has stayed on the diet'. A year later Alex Schauss, also a probation officer, published his book *Diet, Crime, and Delinquency* in which he claimed equally high success rates among juvenile delinquents in his part of California.

Schauss's book was a best-seller, and quite a few probation departments across America started to copy his low-sugar policy for some of their offenders. But unfortunately there was very little hard evidence to prove that Schauss or Reed were right.

The problem was this: it was perfectly possible that the improvement in the offenders wasn't due to the effect of the diet at all, but was due to purely psychological reasons. No one had done any proper experiments to find out.

As a result, most criminologists dismissed the theory. And, given their background, who can blame them? All criminologists, myself included, have been trained to believe that behaviour is determined by the society we live in. Look up any standard criminology textbook, and you'll find virtually no mention of diet and crime. One leading textbook does give the subject four lines, only to rule out the likelihood of there being any biological component to criminal behaviour.

But a good scientist should never rule out anything before it is properly tested, and I determined that the low-sugar diet theory needed proper scientific evaluation. After all, the idea was becoming very popular among professional probation officers, but without any real evidence to back it up. So the idea had to be examined fully, and either refuted or supported.

Either result would be beneficial to society. If Schauss and Reed were recommending ineffective intervention, they were wasting time and money spent on staff training and were asking prisoners to sacrifice sugar for no good reason. More importantly, if Schauss and Reed were wrong, they were causing probation officers to divert their limited efforts from other known, successful treatment strategies. On the other hand, if Schauss and Reed were right, the implications would be far reaching. If a simple dietary change could

---

The Tidewater Experimental Diet

Before   *After*

BREAKFAST

orange tang (fizzy drink)   orange juice
pre-sweetened dry cereal   oatmeal with fruit
french toast with syrup   wholewheat pancakes with
whole milk   syrup
                                  skimmed milk

MORNING SNACKS

soft drink   tomato/orange/pineapple
potato crisps   juice
glazed doughnuts   celery and carrots
                                  fresh cheese with apples

LUNCH

cheeseburger with bun   roast chicken
macaroni/egg salad   tossed salad with dressing
chips   boiled potato
chocolate cream pie   fruit
hot chocolate made with   skimmed milk
    whole milk

---

prevent a young person from adopting a life of crime, the cost savings alone would be immense – locking up one single adult criminal currently costs the US taxpayer $35,000 (£20,000) a year.

Still, I was pretty sceptical, feeling in my bones that there was no way diet could affect criminal behaviour – after all, that's what all the experts said, and that's what I had been taught at university, so it was almost unimaginable to believe that all my teachers and all those experts could be wrong.

I went back to Frank Kern with a plan of action. I would use the detention centre he ran at Tidewater, Virginia as the

Before	*After*
AFTERNOON SNACKS	
two soft drinks	fruit juice
potato crisps	mixed nuts
sweets	peanut butter/honey
cupcakes	wholegrain bread
	crackers
DINNER	
cheese and onion pizza	Lasagna
shredded lettuce	tossed salad with dressing
biscuits	toasted garlic buns
ice cream	sherbet
Kool-aide (fizzy drink) or	skimmed milk or
sweetened ice tea	unsweetened ice tea
EVENING SNACKS	
ice cream	popcorn
soft drinks	peanuts and other nuts
sweets	cheeses and cold meat
pastries	fruit
potato crisps	sugar-free soft drinks

test bed. We should change the children's diet for three months to see what happened. He readily agreed.

Tidewater was ideal: it was small, with only about fifteen inmates, so the experiment was simple to arrange. Another advantage was that the children were a shifting population; being merely a remand centre, the average length of stay was less than three weeks. So any change of diet would not be noticed by most of them – once it had changed, new inmates would be totally unaware that there was an experiment going on. Thirdly, the kids at Tidewater were fed the typical American juvenile diet – precisely the kinds of high-sugar foods Schauss and Reed claimed caused crime. Finally, because Frank Kern had a reputation as a health food nut, it was easy to make the staff believe that the diet change was not part of an experiment to test its effect on behaviour, but simply because Frank was a nut!

So on 8 March 1981, the experimental diet was begun, and we held our breath to see what would happen.

Wham! A honey-pot hit the wall, spreading its contents lugubriously down the brickwork. The kids were furious, and complained loudly. So did the staff, but somewhat more privately. However, they were professional enough to maintain discipline. The staff told the children that they did not agree with the administration's new diet, but that there were many laws and rules in society that people do not like that must be obeyed. Along similar lines, this rule was to be obeyed . . . or else! By the end of the day, the children had stopped grumbling and it became apparent that we were not going to provoke a riot.

Three months after the diet policy-change, the administrator called his weekly staff meeting. Without looking at the data in the files, everyone had noticed that the youths' behaviour had improved tremendously. Approximately five groups of juveniles had come and gone over the previous three months and each group had been better behaved than those confined in Tidewater before 8 March. In a debriefing session, the administrator asked his counsellors if they any idea why these juveniles were better behaved. This question was important because, if the staff were doing something differently to account for the behaviour change, they needed to continue to do it.

One counsellor joked that they had entered a new astrological age on 21 March, and that may have been responsible for the change. There were a number of suggested explanations, but interestingly not one staff member suggested that the changes in behaviour may have been caused by the new diet. This confirmed that we had been successful in diverting attention away from the possibility that diet influences behaviour. The administrator then briefed his staff about the study. He told them that the intention of the new diet was to determine if the changes would produce a decrease in reports of bad behaviour. He told them that 'incident reports' had decreased by forty-five per cent since early March. The staff confirmed that none of them thought that the study was the reason why Frank made the dietary changes and no one suspected that an experiment was in progress.

I was astounded and excited. It appeared that the lay people might be right, and that we scientists were wrong. I experienced the same emotional high that explorers must have felt when they discovered new continents. Nevertheless, my training checked my enthusiasm and I returned to the data to look for alternative reasons why the low-sugar group may have done better.

First, could the improvement in behaviour have been due to psychological effects – the so-called Experimenter, Pygmalion, Hawthorne, and Placebo Effects? These are wicked traps for the unwary which can make an experiment appear to work when it really hasn't. It's all to do with expectation: if people expect something to work, they will often behave in a way that fulfils the expectation.

The 'Experimenter' effect is when the person running the experiment desires a certain outcome, and unconsciously

in this case, that wasn't possible: first, I
...d the experiment to fail, but it didn't. Sec-
...ata on the children's behaviour was collected
...emselves in the form of daily written reports of

fig 1

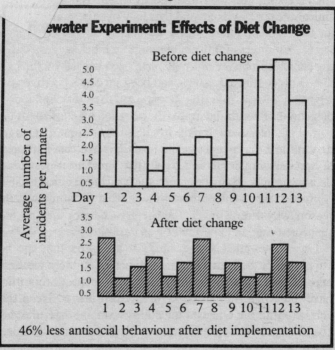

...ewater Experiment: Effects of Diet Change

46% less antisocial behaviour after diet implementation

bad behaviour. I took no part at all. What about the staff
themselves, could they have been expecting improvements –
the 'Pygmalion' effect? Answer, no: as the debriefing session
showed, none of them connected the diet change with the
kids' improved behaviour. Next, the 'Hawthorne' effect: the
desire of the participants to please the experimenter and
produce the desired results. But that again was also ruled out
– no one knew an experiment was going on in the first place.
Lastly, the 'Placebo' effect – the children might have

behaved better because they expected themselves to improve. However, I came to the conclusion that there was no chance of placebo effects, either. The staff was asked if any of them had heard the children tell others that the sugar-free diet had a therapeutic effect on behaviour. No one had. In order for a placebo effect to be responsible for the improvements, a bizarre sequence of events would have had

---

Measuring Bad Behaviour

All prisons in the United States are required to make a detailed record of every 'antisocial act' committed by every prisoner in a so-called 'incident report' book. These 'incidents' range from violent assaults on staff as the most serious, through vandalism and theft, to more innocuous bad behaviour like verbal abuse or insubordination. Because making these reports is mandatory on all prison staff, the incident reports are about as complete and objective a record of an inmate's behaviour as it is possible to get.

---

to occur. First, at least one of the fourteen children present in the facility when the change was implemented would have had to have heard that sugar might cause crime. Second, the child would have had to have believed it. Third, the child would have had to relay this belief to the other children. Fourth, the subsequent groups of inmates would have had to accept the belief system. Finally, the children of every group would have had to communicate this belief system to the next group of children without the staff ever hearing about it. In short, I concluded that this explanation was a virtual impossibility.

Thus I felt we had successfully eliminated psychological effects as an explanation for the reduction in behaviour problems. That had been the main problem with all the previous research, and so this was a real step forward.

But we still couldn't be sure. For one thing, our numbers were dangerously small, with just twenty-four subjects on a low-sugar diet to compare with thirty-four on a standard diet before the diet policy-change. Was it possible that these twenty-four children were just a statistical fluke? Was it possible that they were simply better-adjusted children before they ever even started the diet? Frank and I decided that these preliminary results justified continuing with the new diet and analysing its effects further. We decided to compare the results of juveniles who were confined the previous year with juveniles who were going to be confined the next year. This comparison would give us a larger sample size and allow us to control for the possibility that the low-sugar group exhibited less violence even before entering the institution.

We continued to control for psychological effects by not informing the staff that we would again be pulling the next year's records. We also noted which counsellors thought that the diet was responsible for the changes in behaviour and which counsellors thought that the relationship was impossible. It would be simple to determine statistically if the staff members who accepted the diet and crime link would be writing fewer reports than those who denied that a relationship could exist.

At the end of a whole year on the new diet, I finally had records of 174 children, and was able to compare them with the records of the 102 children on the previous year's standard diet. The data showed that 102 juveniles on the standard institution diet produced 29.4 incidents per juvenile per 100 days, and the 174 juveniles on the modified (low-sugar) diet produced 15.3 incidents per juvenile per 100 days. Again, the children on the new low-sugar diet had committed forty-six per cent fewer antisocial acts than the children on the old diet. So the experiment had worked a second time. This was beginning to get really interesting.

Nevertheless, my training checked my enthusiasm and I returned to the data to look for alternative reasons why the low-sugar group may have done better. Although I was convinced that I had controlled for all possible psychological effects, I concluded that the 174 children on the low-sugar diet could simply have been a better-behaved group than the 102 children on the standard diet. This alternative explanation for the difference in antisocial behaviour had to be examined very closely.

I started by looking at the reasons why the children were sent to the Tidewater Detention Center in the first place. Their behaviour prior to Tidewater should have correlated with their behaviour in the institution. Some of them had committed violent crimes such as robbery, and assault and battery. Others had committed property crimes such as larceny, burglary, and car theft. The children on the low-sugar diet who had been confined for violent crimes or property offences did better than those on the standard diet who were confined for similar crimes. The same pattern held for children who were 'status offenders'. These were children who had been neglected, abused, or had run away from home. In short, these results indicated that the children who had been on the standard diet were not more prone to violent acts than those on the sugar-free diet.

I also examined the distribution of ages in each of the groups. I found that the younger children tended to commit the most offences in the institution. Thus, the loss of older children among the group who received the standard diet might have been responsible for the difference between the groups. However, this could not explain the results when I compared thirteen-year-old children in both groups followed by the comparison of the fourteen-year-old, fifteen-year-old, and sixteen-year-old children. In each age group, the children on the standard diet committed more incidents than the children on the low-sugar diet.

Last, but not least, I examined the racial makeup of both groups to see if the juvenile's race might be responsible for the low-sugar diet group producing less antisocial behaviour.

I found that the non-white population committed more antisocial behaviour on the standard diet. This was consistent with national crime rates. However, both whites and non-whites showed lower levels of antisocial behaviour in the low-sugar group than the whites and non-whites in the standard diet group.

At that point in time, I felt confident that the forty-six per cent lower rate of antisocial behaviour in the low-sugar group was not due to psychological effects nor to the fact that these juveniles were better behaved prior to their imprisonment. Frank Kern reported that the low-sugar diet policy had actually saved the institution thirty-nine per cent of its food budget, which was a secondary bonus to the study.

In 1983 I published these results under the title 'Diet and Crime: An Empirical Examination of the Value of Nutrition in the Control and Treatment of Incarcerated Juvenile Offenders' in the *International Journal of Biosocial Research*.

The impact of that paper took me completely by surprise. First my university was not at all pleased, they told me that my type of research was not good sociology.

But elsewhere the reaction was more favourable. Frank Kern had sent our project to the State Council of Governments in Kentucky where it won an award as one of the twenty most innovative programmes in the United States. The research was also broadcast on all three major United States television networks. Network television came from as far as London and Australia to cover the Tidewater study.

Junk Food

'Junk food causes crime' was the typical message that the press took from the Tidewater data, but of course that was far too simplistic a conclusion. What we had shown, and I repeat to my great surprise, was that a low-sugar diet reduced 'antisocial behaviour' in a juvenile prison population.

So I felt that it was time to get acquainted with some of the basic nutritional facts about sugar.

First, what is sugar? There are two major kinds; the refined and the unrefined. Unrefined sugars are found naturally in many of the foods we eat. They often occur in combination with other nutrients like proteins, fats, vitamins and minerals. Refined sugars have been deliberately extracted from food (mainly sugar-cane and beet) so that they contain little or nothing of the other nutrients they were originally combined with.

How much refined sugar does the average American or Briton eat? One of the first things I discovered was that in one year, the average American drinks 395 cans of soft drinks. Children drink more than adults, and boys drink far more than girls. It is not uncommon for some delinquent children to be drinking between six and twelve cans a day! A single twelve-ounce can of a popular soft drink contains nine teaspoons of sugar. Some contain even more. So obviously, cutting out soft drinks at Tidewater had been a major sugar eliminator. I also found out that getting rid of the breakfast cereal was pretty important too – most packeted breakfast cereals contain fifty per cent sugar, and some even seventy per cent! In fact much of the processed food we buy contains sugar added by the manufacturer, but often hidden to the consumer. Sugar is obviously a major ingredient in things like doughnuts, pastries, biscuits, cakes, ice creams, and confectionery, but did you know it's also in a whole lot of savoury foods like white bread, processed peas, cheese snacks, baked beans, and tomato ketchup?

So it's not surprising that the average person in Great Britain and America currently gets twenty-four per cent of his/her daily calories from sugars! Today, we consume 139 pounds of sugar per person each year, which is more than twice the level recommended by the experts in nutrition.

Added Sugar in Common Processed Foods

Food	Portion	Sugar content (tsp)
Cola drinks	12 oz	9
Orange squash	12 oz	11.5
Tonic water	8 oz	5.5
Jam	1 tbsp	4–6
Milk chocolate bar	1.5 oz	2.5
Chewing gum	1 stick	.5
Hard sweets	4 oz	20
White bread	1 slice	.5
Cornflakes	1 bowl with tsp sugar	4–8
Hamburger bun	1	3
Hotdog bun	1	3
Fruit cake	4 oz	5
Sweet biscuits	1	1.5
Chocolate éclair	1	7
Doughnut, plain	1	3
Doughnut, glazed	1	6
Baked beans	1 small tin	2.5
Tinned spaghetti	1 small tin	1.5
Tomato ketchup	1 tablespoon	.75
Processed peas	1 small can	.25
Tomato soup	½ can	1
Chutney	2 tablespoons	3.5
Meatballs in onion and gravy	½ can	.25
Sweetcorn	⅓ can	1.5
Plain pastry	1 (4 oz)	3

The Sugar Ball Starts Rolling

The publicity generated by the Tidewater study reached the ears of prison administrations across America. They were impressed not only by the fact that the new low-sugar diet appeared to improve behaviour, but also because there was a considerable financial saving – less sugar costs less! Alabama was the first state to go low-sugar, making the new diet compulsory in every one of its juvenile institutions. Before long, California followed suit.

I was called in to Alabama to assess the effects of the new diet at one of their remand centres in Coosa Valley, and found improvements similar to Tidewater – an average reduction of thirty-five per cent in antisocial behaviour. But again, like Tidewater the number of children I was able to get data on was small. What I urgently needed was a much bigger study to convince myself, let alone any of the thousands of other sceptical scientists out there, that there really was a cast-iron connection between the new diet and the children's better behaviour. The golden opportunity presented itself in California.

Nowhere in the United States are the sides drawn more sharply on nutrition and behaviour than southern California. That area manufactures and exports more health-oriented products than any other region in the United States. Californians consume more health foods than other segments of the US population. Also, southern California is the headquarters for numerous alternative health-care organisations. On the other hand, this region also contains an organisation that specialises in combating 'health-fraud' claims made by the other health-oriented organisations!

One of the prime targets of the 'health-fraud' lobby was the idea that sugar causes crime, and so when in April 1981 the Los Angeles County probation department decided to go low-sugar, it caused serious ructions. The 'health-fraud' critics attacked the probation department for adopting a policy that had no scientific basis whatever, and accused them of indulging in wishful thinking.

The attacks mounted, and the probation department decided to ask me to analyse their data, and verify whether the new diet had really had any effect. When Los Angeles implemented their low-sugar diet policy the probation department were running three large borstals and fifteen smaller juvenile camps. Because of our low budget, we decided to focus exclusively on the three large juvenile halls and to select randomly three camps to participate in the analysis.

On 1 April 1981, the day that the low-sugar diet was implemented, the three borstals held 1382 juveniles. This was in marked contrast to the twelve to fifteen prisoners typically housed in Tidewater or Coosa Valley. The larger number of prisoners made it possible to eliminate what I thought to be the greatest weakness of the previous studies. I wanted to make sure that the improved behaviour in those studies could not be attributed to the possibility that the juveniles on the low-sugar diet were simply better behaved. For the first time, there were enough children in the sites at the time of the diet change to compare each child's behaviour before and after the diet policy was implemented. In effect, each child served as his own control, which ensured that the two 'groups' were identical in race, sex, prior criminal histories, etc. I examined each child's behaviour reports three months before and after the new diet policy (see fig 2).

My analysis showed that the 1382 juveniles produced a forty-four per cent reduction in official 'incident reports'. The likelihood that this could occur by chance was less than one in ten thousand! The pattern was identical in all three borstals. The 173 offenders in the three juvenile camps after the diet policy change produced fifty-four per cent fewer official incident reports than the 194 offenders in the camps before the policy change. Thus, all six sites showed an improvement in behaviour after the low-sugar diet policy was implemented.

The possibility that the improvements were due to psychological effects was readily dismissed. First, the probation

fig 2

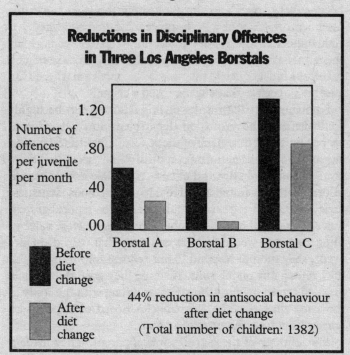

Reductions in Disciplinary Offences in Three Los Angeles Borstals

Number of offences per juvenile per month

1.20
.80
.40
.00

Borstal A   Borstal B   Borstal C

Before diet change

After diet change

44% reduction in antisocial behaviour after diet change
(Total number of children: 1382)

department staff were overwhelmingly opposed to the diet policy-change because they had not been consulted on the issue. They, much like the staff at Tidewater, strongly resented the policy and felt that they were being forced to shove the diet down the juveniles' throats. The staff, therefore, did not expect behaviour to improve. Indeed, many of them said they thought things would get worse and that they were concerned that fights would break out when the sugar was taken away. In fact, I did find one case where this happened. A mother brought a bag of jelly beans into the facility to give to her son. A probation officer stopped her and informed her that her son could not have the jelly beans because they contained sugar. He explained that sugary foods were now considered to be contraband. She apparently became very angry and started beating the officer over the head with the bag of jelly beans, saying that she knew her rights and that the facility could not keep her from giving them to her son. She was finally booked on assault and battery. I must concede that this is the only case where I am absolutely certain that sugar caused a crime!

Knowing that the results of this study would be highly controversial, the probation department and I decided to share a tentative final draft of the report with selected professionals who had been the most critical of the theory that there is a relationship between diet and crime. We asked them to inform us if they found any errors in our methods, statistics, logic, or analysis so that we could change the report before it was released to the general public. Perhaps we were naïve to think that they would feel the same way that we did. In any event, they did not respond to our request for input nor did they return our phone calls. Instead, they gave the media a detailed report on what they felt was wrong with the study at the same time that the Los Angeles Board of Supervisors released the final report to the press.

The strategy of these critics was apparent. They made a large number of criticisms that would take very little effort for anyone to explain and dismiss. But the criticisms were so numerous that they gave the impression that the work was poor. After wading through them all, I did find one very legitimate criticism. There was the possibility that the juveniles' behaviour was already improving as their length of stay progressed. I had not looked at this possibility before, so I went back to the data and examined it. I found no evidence to suggest that the juveniles confined before the transition date were becoming less prone to antisocial behaviour the longer that they stayed in the institution. For example, those juveniles who were confined throughout January, February, and March committed approximately the same number of serious incidents each month. But in April, May, and June, they committed forty-four per cent fewer incidents. Thus, there was no evidence that the juveniles were simply becoming better behaved over time before the diet policy went into effect.

There are several other characteristics of the study that I wish had been published in the original article. Although the 1382 cases produced a forty-seven per cent reduction in antisocial behaviour, in fact all the changes in behaviour occurred in just sixteen per cent of the population. It turned out that only 221 juveniles were responsible for all the reductions in antisocial behaviour. This means that major changes occurred, but with only a few.

A second very important finding that was never published in the original article was the fact that the low-sugar diet worked with boys but not girls. Out of the 1382 juveniles, just 139 were female. The females' rate of antisocial behaviour before the diet change was identical to their rate after the diet change.

I did publish a breakdown of the types of crimes that were committed by the 1382 juveniles prior to their placement in a county juvenile hall. A relationship between the crime and later improvement in behaviour existed across all types of offenders. Killers, rapists, burglars, drug abusers, and those who stole people's property all showed a reduction in antisocial acts. In 1983, however, I failed to emphasise the fact that drug abusers and repeat offenders showed the greatest improvements in behaviour. In retrospect, this information turned out to be a vital clue for uncovering the reasons why some children responded to the low-sugar diet better than others.

The Los Angeles study finally convinced me that the

reduction in antisocial behaviour was not because of psychological factors, neither was it a figment of the probation officers' imaginations, nor was it due to chance. If the changes had occurred just once or even twice, I might have been able to accept the idea that an unknown factor played a role in reducing bad behaviour. But, when the same thing occurred nine times in a row, the explanation that an unknown variable might be the cause was too much to swallow. The new diet was definitely related to the improvements in behaviour. The real question was how and why?

2 Is Sugar Really the Culprit?

What conclusions could I draw from my research so far? On the face of it, it seemed that because a low-sugar diet improved behaviour, the sugar itself must be the cause of the initial bad behaviour. That was what Alex Schauss and Barbara Reed believed, and after all they had pioneered the low-sugar diet; it was what many of the probation services believed too, as well as large sections of the press. But I wasn't so sure; there were a number of other possible explanations. By 1983, having taught myself considerably more about nutrition, I was in a position to spell them out.

I reasoned that children could behave worse on a high-sugar diet because:
either

1. Processed sugary foods contain high levels of refined sugar which may cause chronic reactive hypoglycaemia (or low blood sugar), thereby impairing brain function.
or

2. Processed sugary foods often contain food additives (colours, flavours, preservatives, etc.), which may cause an allergic reaction, which in turn may affect the brain.
or

3. Processed sugary foods often contain fewer vitamins and minerals than the foods served in the low-sugar diet; a depleted intake of these nutrients may impair cell metabolism which may in turn impair brain function.

Those were my three possible explanations for the consistent behaviour patterns which I had been documenting. The question now was, which one was correct? Or were all three correct? Or perhaps none of them at all?

Sugar, Additives or Vitamins?

A golden opportunity to put the three possibilities to the test came my way almost immediately. You may remember I said that Alabama was the first state to adopt the new low-sugar non-processed diet throughout its whole juvenile prison system in 1982. They were very keen to monitor its effectiveness, so early in 1984 they contacted me again and asked me to document exactly what changes in behaviour it was producing (see fig 3).

Because money was tight, I decided to limit my investigation to the two largest borstals in Alabama, at Mount Meiggs and Vacca. They housed over two hundred of the most difficult juvenile delinquents in the state, and many of them were serving long sentences. From a research standpoint, this was ideal; it allowed me to examine the same children eighteen months before and eighteen months after the diet policy-change. This strategy enabled the children to serve not only as their own controls as they had in Los Angeles, but it also made it possible for me to identify long-term trends. Examining the long-term changes was the key to understanding why the low-sugar diet worked.

First I looked at the raw data. Sure enough, just like all the previous studies, there was a considerable reduction in incident reports after the diet change – thirty-five per cent fewer antisocial acts at Mount Meiggs and forty-two per cent at Vacca.

The next question I asked was this: how quickly did the reduction in antisocial behaviour occur? Did it happen over hours, days, or months? The answer would give me a very strong clue as to which of the three possible explanations was the right one.

I scanned the incident reports eagerly. I knew that if low blood sugar or reactive hypoglycaemia was the explanation, I

fig 3

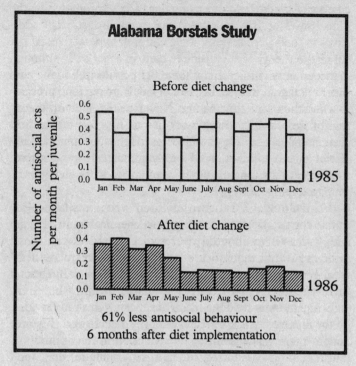

Alabama Borstals Study

Before diet change

1985

Number of antisocial acts per month per juvenile

After diet change

1986

61% less antisocial behaviour
6 months after diet implementation

should expect to find the children's behaviour improving very rapidly – within as little as a few hours. My reasoning was that, after a diet change from high- to low-sugar foods, their blood sugar levels would become normal in just a few minutes, thereby normalising their brain function, and hence stabilising their behaviour almost immediately. So I went straight to the incident reports for Days 1 and 2 after the diet change. But, to my surprise, they showed no reduction at all – the level of antisocial behaviour hadn't been affected.

It was a very significant discovery. It meant that the reactive hypoglycaemia/low blood sugar theory, which was the whole rationale for the diet change, was probably not the primary explanation at all.

So I turned to explanation number two – food additives. In the early 1980s there was a popular theory (promoted by the late Professor Ben Feingold) that modern 'artificial' additives in food were making some children hyperactive. At the time the theory was extremely controversial and, although subsequently vindicated by some British research a few years later, Feingold was getting a lot of flak from the food processors and their scientific mafiosi. Nevertheless, I felt his theory might be relevant to my work as our new low-sugar diet, being made up mainly of unprocessed foods, contained many fewer additives than the old high-sugar diet. It was possible, therefore, that the behaviour changes we were seeing were due to hyperactivity.

Feingold said that when children who are allergic (the more correct word is intolerant) to chemical additives, are changed over to an additive-free diet, they show an initial increase of hyperactivity around four days later, followed by a fairly rapid reduction within the next three days. By the end of about a week, their behaviour should be normal.

So again I searched the incident reports – this time looking at the files for the first ten days after the diet change. But once again, there was absolutely no reduction in the numbers of antisocial acts reported. I had to conclude that food intolerance wasn't the explanation.

I turned to the third explanation – that the cause of improved behaviour was increased consumption of vitamins and minerals in the foods that replaced the high-sugar foods. In other words, the problem might not lie in what was *in* the junk foods, but rather in what was *missing* from them. According to this theory, the immediate increase in vitamins and minerals – as a result of eating more fruit, vegetables, and wholegrain products – would result in the gradual increase of these nutrients in the blood and brain, as deficiencies were corrected. This in turn would produce a gradual reduction in antisocial behaviour.

I went back to the files, and there it was! As the weeks went by after the diet change, I saw a slow but sure reduction in the number of incident reports, the improvement in behaviour peaking at about eighteen weeks and then remaining constant. And I was also glad to see that in Vacca, for example, the sixty-one per cent drop in antisocial behaviour remained constant for the next eighteen months. That finally put to rest any lingering suspicion that it was all psychological – placebo effects don't ever last anything like that long.

So the data strongly suggested that low vitamin and mineral intake could have been the cause of the antisocial behaviour. Still, this was not a definitive conclusion. There was always the outside possibility that glucose or food-intolerance problems were the real culprits. The incident reports may have dropped slowly because once the prisoners' biochemistries were corrected, it may have taken a few weeks for the daily rehabilitative message to take effect. Still, the direction that future research needed to take was clear. Was it possible that poor nutrition was the real culprit that caused violence and antisocial behaviour?

Vitamins and Minerals

Let's take a look, therefore, at the reasons why the low-sugar diet might have been affecting the children's nutrition. To do that we'll need to take a small diversion into history.

Our bodies have changed very little from those of our ancestors who lived in caves thousands of years ago. The process of evolution is a very slow phenomenon. The foods we eat did not change very much either before the industrial revolution and the Enlightenment. But with the rise of science, populations became more urban, cities grew large, and technology changed our culture and our food. We should not forget that the discovery of the New World was caused by the quest to improve our food with spices and other food additives!

Today, two thirds of the food we eat is highly processed

The Nutrients in Food

MACRONUTRIENTS

Proteins are a chain of single units called amino acids.
Amino acids are nitrogen atoms that, when linked together, constitute protein. There are nearly 30 different amino acids. Nine of them cannot be manufactured in adequate quantities and are considered as essential nutrients that must come from food.
Fat contains linoleic acid which is essential for many body functions.
Carbohydrates are composed of carbon, hydrogen, and oxygen. They are the preferred calorie source for the body.

MICRONUTRIENTS

(a) *Vitamins* A, Folic acid, Biotin, Thiamin (B1), Riboflavin (B2), Niacin (B3), Pantothenic acid (B5), Pyridoxine (B6), B12, C, D, E, and K
(b) *Minerals* Calcium, Phosphorus, Chlorine, Potassium, Sulphur, Sodium, Magnesium, Fluorine, Silicon, Vanadium, Chromium, Manganese, Iron, Cobalt, Nickel, Copper, Zinc, Selenium, Molybdenum, Tin, and Iodine.

and only one third is structurally similar to what our forefathers ate. Manufacturers have added colours to make food look better, flavours to make them taste better, odours to improve the smell, preservatives to increase shelf life, and a host of other refinements to make the food sell better than their competitors' products. Unfortunately, a concern for the nutritional value of the food was never a part of the equation in what would sell best.

What has happened to bread illustrates this. Bread is usually made from wheat or, more specifically, the seed grain or berry of wheat. Inside the grain's casing (or chaff) is a thin layer of bran which makes up fourteen per cent of the wheat berry. Inside the bran lies the endosperm that makes up eighty-three per cent of the wheat berry. Near the bottom of the grain, germ is found and makes up the remaining three per cent of the grain. For thousands of years, mankind had separated the grain from the stem, ground it into flour and baked it into bread. By the beginning of this century, however, the companies that ground flour had made several technological breakthroughs, and, with the introduction of new milling processes, the bran as well as the wheat germ was stripped away. All that remained of the wheat berry was the endosperm that made up eighty-three per cent of the grain. The endosperm is the soft, inside portion of the grain that contains starch and proteins. When the endosperm is baked into bread, it forms a stretchy protein called gluten, which traps air bubbles in the bread. The result is a soft, smooth, and light white bread. By 1920, the general public preferred this 'rich man's bread' over the old-fashioned crunchy, dark-brown bread. The manufacturers charged a lot more for the bread because of the increased processing costs of separating the bran and germ. Although this was true, they conveniently forgot to tell the public that they were also able to sell the wheat germ and bran for animal feed at a large profit!

At the turn of the century, no one knew the nutritional consequences of replacing wholegrain bread with white bread. It turns out that the wheat grain is a good source of twenty-two essential vitamins and minerals, but the endosperm contains only four in substantial quantities. The most nutritious part of the grain is the wheat germ. However, the manufacturers eliminated the germ from the bread because they thought that it caused the bread to spoil rapidly. No one knew that the real reason why the bread spoiled was because the fat-soluble vitamins in it became rancid.

The result was that many people became very ill and a few even died for unknown reasons between the world wars. Only then did scientists discover that wheat germ and bran were the primary sources of iron, thiamin, riboflavin, and niacin, which are four essential nutrients for brain function. A number of scientists recommended that these four nutrients be placed back into bread. Initially the food industry fought hard against reinstating these nutrients in bread, but finally agreed. However, now they had the gall to call their bread 'vitamin-enriched'. After all, the number of nutrients had been reduced from twenty-two to only four. As someone once said, 'Would you feel enriched if a robber took your wallet, pulled out twenty-two pounds, and then gave you back four?' Somehow, I find it hard to believe that this experience could be accurately described as 'enrichment'.

Now, forty years later, nutritionists realise that the best bread nutritionally is the old-fashioned, wholegrain bread, and manufacturers are selling it again. It is interesting that today's wholegrain bread is more expensive than white bread when its manufacture costs less. Manufacturers explain this by saying that they can no longer sell the bran and germ separately as animal feed.

There are several important lessons that can be gleaned from the story of how bread processing has changed in this century. First, we must remember that profit is the primary goal of food processors. They try to achieve this goal by increasing the appeal of their product rather than its nutritional quality. Secondly, in the past when industry was confronted with evidence that their processing had lowered the vitamin and mineral content of food, they denied that any damage existed, and fought aggressively against government food regulations. Thus, today we must accept the responsibility to choose foods wisely and realise that the manufacturers' advertising will often be misleading. We could not trust their assurances that the foods they processed were nutritious before, and I can see little evidence to support any other conclusion today.

It is important to point out that not all refined or processed foods have a poor nutrient value. Many highly processed foods are very nutritious. The distinction that most scientists make is between 'dismembered' or 'partitioned' and 'whole' foods, with the latter generally being preferred. A dismembered or partitioned food is any plant or animal in which the tissue that is the primary source of calories has been separated from the tissue that contains most of the vitamins, minerals or amino acids. The best examples of dismembered foods are refined sugars, fats and oils, milled grains (primarily wheat) and alcohol. About two thirds of the calories we consume each day come from dismembered foods. Few people have attempted to define what 'junk' food is. But the closest definition of junk food is: a partitioned or dismembered food that has plenty of calories but little else in the way of micronutrients.

In the light of this let's examine how the new low-sugar borstal diets could have been improving the children's behaviour. The diets consisted mainly of fresh fruit, fresh vegetables, and wholegrain bread – i.e., unprocessed foods from which none of the vitamins and minerals had been dismembered. The previous high-sugar diets consisted of many more processed foods which inevitably contained fewer nutrients.

But how could a shortage of vitamins and minerals produce antisocial behaviour? To explain this, I'm going to have to dive into a little bit of brain chemistry. But it's not vital to the story, and if you'd rather skip it, jump ahead to the next section.

Feeding the Brain

The human brain contains an estimated 100 billion nerve cells and makes up only two per cent of an adult's body weight. Yet, these tiny brain cells use twenty-five per cent of the body's energy requirements! Their constant transmission of electrical impulses accounts for most of the brain's energy use. The brain is different from the other organs in that it stores no energy. In order to function, it needs a constant supply of two major fuels – oxygen and glucose. Oxygen it gets from the air, glucose from food.

Glucose is made in the body and transported via the blood stream to the brain, where it is made to release its energy to power the brain's electrical system. The release of that energy is a two-stage process and is critically dependent on a number of nutrients. The first energy-releasing process – glycolysis – requires the presence of three essential nutrients: niacin, magnesium and phosphorus. The second stage, called the Krebs Cycle (see fig 11, page 124), requires no less than six vitamins – thiamin, riboflavin, niacin, pantothenic acid, biotin, and pyridoxine – and four minerals – iron, magnesium, phosphorus, and manganese.

In addition to the ten nutrients already mentioned, the brain also needs sodium, potassium, and possibly calcium for the actual conduction of nerve impulses. Protein is also essential, as it breaks down into the thirty amino acids that form the brain's chemical neuro-transmitters.

So there are a total of thirteen vitamins and minerals found in food that are absolutely vital for brain function. The brain's ability to produce energy is limited by the quantities of these twelve elements in the cell. Furthermore, since all of these nutrients are required to make energy, you must realise that the nutrient in shortest supply limits energy production. Just as a chain is no stronger than its weakest link, the manufacture of energy is no greater than the single nutrient in shortest supply.

If for any reason energy production falls in the brain, its ability to transmit electrical signals is reduced, and this can cause impaired function. We know this because brain waves, which are nothing more than electrical impulses, change when glucose or oxygen falls too low. The waves become flatter and less frequent. The changes are the most dramatic in the front of the brain which has many more nerve connections and where thought and reasoning are believed to take place.

Nutrition and Behaviour

Now if what I've been saying is true, you would expect to discover that people who have a deficiency of one or more vitamins or minerals may also tend to suffer from disordered thoughts and emotions. And indeed, that is precisely what you find. For example, the leading American textbook for undergraduates in nutrition, *Nutrition, Concepts and Controversies*, states:

Thiamin deficiency can result in 'confusion, uncoordinated movements, depressed appetite, irritability, insomnia, fatigue, and general misery'.

Riboflavin deficiency can result in 'depression, hysteria, psychopathic behaviour, lethargy, and hypochondria before clinical deficiency is detected'.

Niacin deficiency can produce 'irritability, agitated depression, headaches, sleeplessness, memory loss, emotional instability and mental confusion progressing to psychosis or delirium'.

Pyridoxine deficiency can produce 'irritability, insomnia, weakness, mental depression, abnormal brain-wave patterns, convulsions, the mental symptoms of anemia, fatigue, and headaches'.

Folic acid deficiency can result in 'the mental symptoms of anemia, tiredness, apathy, weakness, forgetfulness, mild depression, abnormal nerve function, irritability, headaches, disorientation, confusion, and the inability to perform simple calculations'.

Vitamin B12 deficiency can cause the 'degeneration of the peripheral nervous system'.

Vitamin C deficiency may produce 'hysteria, depression, listlessness, lassitude, weakness, aversion to work, hypochondria, social introversion, possible iron anemia, and fatigue'.

Vitamin A deficiency can cause anemia.

Magnesium deficiency can produce 'apathy, personality changes, and hyperirritability'.

Copper deficiency can produce 'iron-deficiency anemia'.

Zinc deficiency can cause 'poor appetite, failure to grow, iron-deficient anemia, irritability, emotional disorders, and mental lethargy'.

Hamilton, Whitney and Sizer, the authors of this textbook, continue their discussion on nutritional deficiencies and behaviour with the point that many of these nutrients produce very similar symptoms, like depression, weakness, apathy, and withdrawal. In fact, this makes a great deal of sense, because these are the very same nutrients that are required by the brain to convert its fuel into energy. Since the conversion process is limited by the nutrient in shortest supply, it follows that many of them would cause the same symptoms.

As an aside, it is interesting to note that two basic symptoms of neurosis – depression and withdrawal – may be created by nutritional deficiencies. The treatment of choice for neurosis by psychiatrists is the use of an antidepressant drug to increase the firing of neural pathways. It is sad that drug therapy that covers up the underlying cause often takes precedence over conducting a proper nutritional assessment in order to determine if the actual cause of the problem is marginal malnutrition.

Most British and American doctors have no idea that these relationships exist. The average American physician spends four years in pre-med, four years in medical school, one year as an intern, and two years in residence before striking out on his own as a physician. A recent survey indicated that in those eleven years of education, the average doctor attended one third of one course in nutrition. Stated differently, only seven per cent took more than one course! Their formal training was much like my own. Nutrition was ignored. Professionals find it difficult to accept that a major part of their professional training was not adequate.

The obvious solution, to take a lot of vitamins and minerals in order to eliminate possible deficiencies, turns out to be a bad idea. In fact, it can be dangerous! Most people do not understand that too much of some nutrients may be just as dangerous as a deficiency. The trick of getting adequate, but not excessive nutrients, will be discussed in Chapter 10 of this book.

Mental Performance

So my claim that a bad diet can affect behaviour is not so far-fetched as the critics of my work would have you believe. In fact, as I have shown, the idea is supported by a very sound set of theories in a recognised college textbook: low levels of one or more vitamins and minerals can adversely affect glucose metabolism in the brain, leading to impaired mental processes, in turn leading to disorders of thought and emotion – and, I would add, behaviour.

But I also thought: why stop there? Might poor nutrition not also affect a whole range of mental processes? In particular, the so-called cognitive abilities – things like memory, perception, concentration, and learning ability. So I went back to my university textbook on nutrition and looked up those words in the index. And sure enough, there they were:

The Mental Symptoms of Anaemia

Anorexia
Apathy, listlessness
Clumsiness
Conduct disturbances
Decreased attentiveness
Hyperactivity
Irritability
Learning disorders
Lowered IQ
Low scores on vocabulary tests
Low scores on latency and associative reactions
Perceptual restrictions
Reduced physical and work capacity
Repetitive hand and foot movements

NOTE: These symptoms are not caused by anaemia itself, but by iron deficiency in the brain.
SOURCE: *Nutrition, Concepts and Controversies*, p. 440.

My first reaction was to doubt whether iron deficiency was likely to be the whole story, but nevertheless staring me in the face was a list of mental effects that could not only account for the antisocial behaviour I had been seeing in the borstals, but also suggested a whole new line of research – looking at the performance of children in schools.

As had happened so many times before, the right opportunity presented itself.

The Million Kid Experiment

New York City, as everybody knows, has some of the worst social problems in the developed world; the annual murder rate in just one suburb equals the yearly total in the whole of Great Britain! But New York also is one of the most sophisticated cities in the world, and it is often prepared to experiment with new ideas to help solve its social ills.

One of its more enlightened city officials in 1979 was Dr Liz Kagen, the Chief Administrator of the Nutrition Program for the Board of Education. As such, she was in charge of the school meals provided for the two million children who attended the City schools. She had been impressed by the theories of Alex Schauss and Barbara Reed that a high-sugar diet caused behavioural problems, and so in the autumn of 1979 she had issued a set of new nutritional guidelines that transformed the catering service for the whole of New York City. She banned the purchase of any foods that contained more than eleven per cent sucrose, the chemical name for table sugar. The sugar-laden soft drinks went. Sweet-vending machines had to go. Ice cream, milk shakes, and many desserts were no longer allowed.

The manufacturers got scared; they couldn't lose one of their biggest customers. So they set about trying to make their products still taste good while staying within Dr Kagen's eleven per cent sugar limit. For example, the research division of the corporation who sold milk shakes to

New York found that they could meet the eleven per cent sugar limit and still make the drink sweet enough if they replaced some of the sugar with lemon juice. A major manufacturer of doughnuts produced a new line of products that cut sugar sufficiently in their pastries. Thus, it would be misleading to conclude that all 'junk' foods were eliminated by 1980. On the contrary, some were eliminated and others were simply made with less sugar.

Many people have asked how Dr Kagen came to the eleven per cent sucrose rule. She picked this figure by examining the sucrose content of many unprocessed foods and found that they seldom, if ever, contained more than that amount of sucrose. Furthermore, the National Academy of Sciences' Food and Nutrition Board recommended that daily intake of sucrose not exceed ten per cent of the diet. The figure, then, can hardly be construed as excessively restrictive.

But Dr Kagen wasn't prepared to stop there. She wanted to see what kind of effect the diet change was actually having on the pupils, and had put out feelers for some proper research to be carried out.

In April 1983 I happened to be invited to New York to appear on *The Today Show*, NBC's breakfast-time television programme. I arranged to see Dr Kagen that morning; as it turned out, the meeting lasted all day.

I convinced Dr Kagen that it would be relatively inexpensive to examine the impact of her diet policy-changes on academic performance, disciplinary problems, and attendance if the schools maintained good records. By focusing on only the elementary and junior high schools, the analysis could be reduced to 803 schools comprising over a million pupils. In that way I could keep costs down.

I was asked to go ahead, and over the next few months started analysing the data (see fig 4). With over a million children to study, I could hardly examine their individual records. Instead I looked at the results for the whole city of a standard Maths and English test that is given to children in virtually every state in the Union. Called the California Achievement Test (CAT), it ranks how well a school's pupils are doing academically compared to the rest of the nation. For example, a school with a score of fifty per cent in one year would be interpreted as being an average school. During the mid-1970s, New York City schools were receiving CAT scores that averaged forty-one per cent. This means that fifty-nine per cent of their students were performing below grade level, which placed them far below the national average in performance.

I found very little change in scores from year to year for New York City schools. For example, in 1976 they were at the forty-first percentile, in 1977 they stood at forty-three per cent, and in 1978 they had fallen to the thirty-ninth percentile. In fact, over the previous twenty years, the average change between adjacent years when the same test was given was less than one per cent and the greatest gain was two per cent in 1977. This stability was due to the huge number of schools and children that were tested each year.

In the spring of 1979, 1.1 million New York children were performing, on the average, at the thirty-ninth percentile, according to the California Achievement Test. Dr Kagen's low-sugar diet policy was introduced that autumn. She also banned foods containing two artificial food colourings. In the spring of 1980, the children took the CAT again. In one year the children showed a gain to the forty-seventh percentile. This was an average gain of eight per cent! To put this in perspective, that eight per cent increase was the largest documented gain in academic performance on a standardised test in one year on such a large sample.

In the autumn of 1980, Dr Kagen took her diet policies one step further. She banned all remaining non-essential synthetic food colourings and flavours. She also placed modest restrictions on how much fat could be in meats. She did not allow meat that contained more than thirty per cent fat in the children's diet. When the children took the CAT in the spring of 1981, again the scores shot up . . . this time to the fifty-first percentile! In just two years, the New York City schools had produced an average gain of twelve per cent!

fig 4

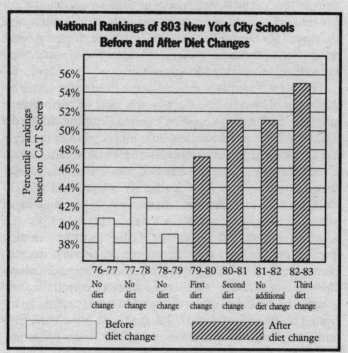

National Rankings of 803 New York City Schools Before and After Diet Changes

Percentile rankings based on CAT Scores

76-77	No diet change
77-78	No diet change
78-79	No diet change
79-80	First diet change
80-81	Second diet change
81-82	No additional diet change
82-83	Third diet change

Before diet change · After diet change

In the autumn of 1981, Dr Kagen made no additional diet policy-changes. In the spring of 1982, there were no changes in CAT scores; they remained at the fifty-first percentile. However, her last major policy-change took place in the autumn of 1982 when she banned foods that contained two preservatives, BHT and BHA. In the spring of 1983, the CAT scores jumped for the third time in twenty years. This time they reached the fifty-fifth percentile.

In short, in the three years that Dr Kagen restricted selected types of food, the number of children who could read and do maths at grade level rose by a total of sixteen per cent. In contrast, before these diet policy-changes, the largest increase between any two adjacent years was under two per cent. In view of the previous track record, the sixteen per cent gain in just three years was truly amazing; it meant that over 160 000 children in New York were able to read and do maths at or above their grade level for the first time immediately following Dr Kagen's diet policy-changes.

The New York data showed other impressive features. The most dramatic finding was the gain in performance among children who could be deemed 'learning disabled'. The term has many definitions, but for purposes of the New York study, it referred to students whose performance scores placed them two or more grades below where they should have been. In 1979, New York City schools had 124 000 children who met this definition. They were children in serious academic difficulty, and were expected to become school drop-outs. The percentage of children with scores this low had not changed very much over the previous decade. However, after Dr Kagen had completed her diet policy-changes, the number of children who were performing two or more grades below where they should have been had fallen from 124 000 to just 49 000. In short, the New York City schools did something that allowed 75 000 failures to become successes!

However, a careful scientist would not jump to the conclusion that the academic improvements were due to a change in diet simply because all gains took place during the three years that the diet was revised. The changes in diet may have coincided with other new policies; perhaps the New York City officials did something else that caused the gains in academic performance to occur. So how could I discover if the academic improvement was really due to the diet and nothing else?

Diet and Academic Performance – The Breakthrough

While looking through the New York records, I happened to notice a pile of innocuous-looking documents in a corner. Being naturally inquisitive (as you will by now already have realised!), I looked to see what they were. One set of papers turned out to contain a record of the academic performance of each school. Useful, I thought. But close by, there was another bound loose-leaf folder. I opened it up idly, and my heart immediately began to pound. It was the city's school catering records, and it gave the figures for the number of meals given by each school, and the percentage of children who received daily meals from the school cafeteria.

This was just the kind of information I was looking for. With it I could definitely establish whether or not the change of diet was really connected with the improvement in academic performance.

My reasoning was straightforward. By comparing the schools where very few children ate cafeteria food to those schools where nearly every child ate cafeteria food, I could control for all non-dietary factors simultaneously. I also knew that I could examine the relationship between how much school food was eaten and academic performance for all 803 schools, both before and after the diet changes.

I started by looking at the gain in academic performance that occurred between the spring of 1977 and 1978. I chose that period because the 1.7 per cent improvement represented the largest gain in any year during the decade prior to the change in diet policy. More specifically, I wanted to see how much better the 1978 scores were than the 1977 scores based on the percentage of children in each school who received cafeteria food. All I had to do was subtract the 1977 score from the 1978 score to determine each school's academic gain. The results are shown in the following table.

Changes in Academic Performance before and after the Change of Diet

Percentage of students receiving school food	Average academic gain	Number of schools
ORIGINAL DIET		
under 70%	2.3%	445
70% to 80%	2.2%	102
80% to 90%	1.7%	123
over 90%	−0.6%	133
NEW DIET		
under 70%	7.7%	348
70% to 80%	10.7%	132
80% to 90%	11.7%	161
over 90%	12.2%	162

You will notice that the more students who ate the original poor quality cafeteria food, the poorer their academic performance. In fact, the table shows that the 133 schools where over 90 per cent of the children received school food produced a 0.6 per cent decline in academic performance. Whereas, other schools whose pupils had eaten less school food produced a gain in academic performance.

Although these figures can be interpreted as suggesting that diet makes a difference in academic performance, this is not the only legitimate interpretation. The schools where more children received food may have done worse because they could have represented a lower socio-economic segment of society, and poorer children would not be expected to do so well.

However, this alternative explanation broke down when I made the same comparison after the diet policy had been in effect for four years. What I did was to take the average academic performance for the spring of 1978, and compare it with the average performance during 1980–1983.

The table shows that this time, with the better quality cafeteria food, the more students who ate it, the more academic performance increased. The likelihood that this relationship is due to a statistical coincidence is less than one chance in 100 000! This table may be the most important finding in this book so far as it proves that the improvements in academic performance during the three years were associated with how much cafeteria food was eaten. For the sceptics who find this conclusion impossible to believe, they must answer the following question: if diet and academic performance are not related, how come, before the diet revisions, the schools where more cafeteria food was served improved the least, while after the diet revisions, the schools where more cafeteria food was served improved the most?

It is not surprising that representatives of the sugar industry from as far west as Australia and as far east as England and South Africa have sought me out to examine the data. To date, no one has ever been able to answer that question. The closest anyone has come is to point out that a moderate increase in the number of children who received school food did occur during those years, but that still does not explain why the *direction* of the relationship shifted.

I am often asked how much of New York City's gains can be linked to the diet change. That is impossible to measure precisely, but one can make an educated estimate. My detailed analysis of the 1983 cafeteria records showed that over 160 schools had managed to get their pupils to eat the new low-sugar school diet, while about 30 others had failed almost totally. The contrast in academic achievement was striking: the school examination records showed a clear correlation between the better diet and higher academic performance. Just compare the figures in this next chart.

Comparison of Academic Performance in Schools with High and Low School Cafeteria Attendance

Percentage of children eating new school diet	Average academic gain	Number of schools
under 10%	4.4%	29
over 90%	12.2%	162

These figures also enable one to make a rough estimate of how much the new low-sugar diet actually contributed to the improvement in academic performance. If one assumes that most of the four per cent gain in the 29 schools was due to factors other than diet (since so few of the children at those schools ate school food), one can subtract that from the twelve per cent gain in the 162 schools, and arrive at approximately the amount of change that was associated with eating more school food, i.e. eight per cent. In other words, our best estimate of the influence on diet on the improvement in the New York City School performance would be that considerably more than half of it was associated with eating better food.

Was Sugar the Culprit this Time?

Dr Kagen's whole motive for changing the school meals in New York was because she thought the children were eating too much sugar. But was the low-sugar diet the real reason why the children improved so much academically? Just as in my borstal studies, there were three main considerations that led me to the conclusion that it probably wasn't.

First, there was nothing in the scientific literature to suggest that sugar has any toxic effects. If the evidence exists, I have not been able to find it. And trust me on this, I have looked for such evidence very carefully. If we are going to believe that a simple molecule made of sugar has the ability to impair brain function, then it must fit with what we know about the anatomy and physiology of the brain. But it doesn't.

Second, the effect may have been a coincidence. Apart from reducing sugar, the new school diet also sharply restricted many chemical additives in the food. The foods that contain the most sugar tend to contain the most chemicals. For example, one brand of ice cream that was no longer allowed because of its high-sugar content also contained nearly 400 chemical additives in the forms of synthetic colours, flavours, binders, etc. Who can say if the sugar or some of these chemicals was the culprit? It is very easy and convenient to point a finger at sugar and say that it caused the changes, but if we are going to be honest, we should admit that no one really knows if the cuts in sugar or in the other food additives were primarily responsible for the improvements.

The reduction in sugar or food additives were not the only explanations. The improvements may have been due to having given the children a sufficient supply of vitamins and minerals – when high-sugared foods were eliminated, they were replaced with more nutritious foods. Therefore, it is possible that the improvements were caused by the increased consumption of vegetables, milk and fruit rather than by the decrease in canned drinks.

In actual fact, there is no reason to assume that the cause had to be just one of the above three possibilities. It is possible that it was the combination of eliminating sugar and food additives, and increasing vitamin/mineral consumption that caused the improvements in school performance.

But there was an additional reason why I couldn't come to a definitive conclusion about the New York results: the study unfortunately had some important limitations which were unavoidable. Research in the field of education is notoriously difficult; there are a whole host of factors to take into account – in theory the results could have been distorted by anything from social background to the weather! So, despite the fact that the research design I had used was the best one available (technically it was called a quasi-experimental time-series design), it still could not give a definitive answer.

Nevertheless, the New York study must rank as one of the biggest-ever experiments in nutrition. And what it showed was pretty stunning too: on the face of it, it appeared that changing to a low-sugar diet resulted in an average increase in academic performance of eight per cent.

But, as with the prison behaviour, I couldn't be certain about what the actual cause of the improvements really was.

Naturally I had my own theories; first my prison studies, and now the New York study, coupled with my growing understanding of nutrition, were making me suspect that malnutrition in the form of marginal vitamin and mineral deficiency was the explanation. However, I needed to do much more digging before I could be sure; in particular I needed a simpler experimental testbed than a school situation, and one in which the environment and the diet were much more controlled. What better place than my old haunts – prisons!

3   Testing the Malnutrition Theory

Getting permission to do research in prisons is not an easy matter at the best of times. But, now that I wanted to initiate research of my own, rather than simply evaluating a diet change that had already taken place, things were doubly difficult. Nevertheless by 1985 I had managed to get permission to do a series of special nutritional studies at four different borstals across the USA.

My plan was this: instead of looking at the institution's diet and behaviour as a whole, I would now focus on the specific diet of each individual inmate, and see if there was any connection between what he ate and how he behaved. Specifically, I would try and assess exactly how well or badly nourished he was, and see if that tallied with his behaviour. To do that meant being able to know precisely what he ate.

That's where being in a prison situation was so useful. This totally controlled environment, where the prisoner's food was given to him willy-nilly every day, meant I could find out exactly what he ate. However, I first had to get the catering staff on my side.

What I asked the caterers to do was, for one week, to offer a choice to the prisoners of identical-size portions of all the available foods at every meal – breakfast, lunch and dinner. These could range from the very nutritious – things like wholegrain bread, fruit, and fresh vegetables – to the very un-nutritious – canned drinks, snack foods and the like. It didn't matter how much or little each prisoner ate. However, there were four rules: a. no food swapping allowed, b. second helpings only when supervised, c. all food left-overs to remain at the table at each inmate's assigned seat, d. purchases of between-meal snacks to be recorded.

Thus, the calculation of each prisoner's dietary intake was simple: quantity of foods served minus quantity of foods not eaten equals intake.

Working out the nutritional content was equally simple. Nutritionists have written very useful computer programs that give the exact nutritional content of any foodstuff, from apples to zebra meat. So all we had to do was enter into the computer the weight of every item of food consumed by each prisoner, and out came a list of all the nutrients (i.e. vitamins and minerals) he had eaten that week.

I say it was simple, but it was a mammoth job. Fortunately, at the first borstal I studied in California, I had the help of one of my graduate students, Steve Stinnet. He analysed the food intake of eighty inmates, and then got hold of their 'incident reports' for the previous year.

The results were strikingly neat: the fourteen worst-behaved inmates had consumed significantly lower quantities of twelve essential nutrients than the best or average behaved groups. By contrast, the eighteen best-behaved inmates had consumed more of the twelve nutrients than the children with average behaviour.

Our second study at a detention centre in Virginia produced the same results: the best-behaved inmates consumed more vitamins and minerals than average, the worst-behaved less than average.

And we found exactly the same pattern at a borstal in Oklahoma.

When I published these results, the legislature of the State of New York thought the findings so significant that they ordered a similar study to be done on over 160 of their adult prisoners, housed in a medium security prison; these guys had a reputation as a pretty violent lot. But sure enough, when the nutritional content of what each inmate ate was analysed, yet again the more violent the prisoner the lower the amount of vitamins and minerals in the food he ate.

Now remember, each prisoner was given exactly the same choice of foods ranging from the very nutritious to the very un-nutritious. They had a totally free choice about what and how much they ate. Since the more violent prisoners were consuming fewer vitamins and minerals, it followed that they were *choosing* to eat foods that had a lower nutritional content. In other words, the more violent the prisoner, the more he liked junk food.

That was the first very interesting finding. The second was that, when we ran the data for each vitamin and mineral through the computer, no single individual nutrient showed up as being more important than any other. At first puzzled, when I thought about it, it made sense for two reasons. If the lack of one particular vitamin or mineral was responsible for increased violence, you can bet your bottom dollar nutritionists would have discovered it years ago. Secondly, remembering the part nutrients play in brain chemistry, I knew that a great number of vitamins and minerals were involved; so it was unlikely that any single one would predominate – they would all have their part to play.

If my reasoning was right, that would mean that if an inmate was deficient in just one – any one, it didn't matter – of the vitamins and minerals involved in brain function, then that person would be more likely to be badly behaved or violent.

To test this theory, I went back to the diet records of all the inmates in the four prisons I had recently studied – a grand total of over 300 prisoners – and separated out those prisoners who, I was fairly certain, were deficient in one (or more) nutrients. I then looked at their incident report files. Eureka! I found that ninety per cent of these malnourished inmates had been booked for bad behaviour, whereas the rest of the prisoners had been much better behaved – their behaviour record was almost twice as good.

I was now beginning to feel I was on the right track; it was looking much more likely that vitamin and mineral deficiency was the real culprit. I sat back to contemplate my next move.

I reasoned that, if the prisoners behaved worse the fewer vitamins and minerals were in their food, I should be able to make them behave better by making sure they got more vitamins and minerals.

How could I do that? Obviously, I could make them eat better food. But problems: a. I knew many of them might not eat it – they preferred junk food, and b. I would be back to square one, not knowing if it was the low sugar or the vitamins in the better food that were causing any improvement.

There was only one answer: to give the prisoners the vitamins and minerals they lacked in pill form. That way I could be sure what extra nutrients they were getting. It was the only way of proving whether my theory was correct.

So, armed with boxes of vitamin and mineral pills (the proper term is food supplements), I went back to the borstals in California and Oklahoma, and asked the staff to give every inmate a pill a day. I reckoned a month or so on the supplements would be long enough to get their vitamin and mineral levels up to normal.

Six weeks later I returned, desperate to see whether there had been any change in the kids' behaviour.

As soon as I walked through the prison gates in Oklahoma I knew I had done it. The staff were beaming; the place had never been quieter! I got out the incident report files for the six weeks before the pill-taking period, and then the files for the six weeks period itself. The records of the children who had been booked for antisocial behaviour in the pre-pill period showed a staggering forty-three per cent drop in the number of incidents.

I was thunderstruck; it was pretty much the same level of improved behaviour as in my very first studies. Then, as you may remember, I had consistently found that the change-over to a low-sugar diet had also resulted in an improvement in behaviour of roughly forty per cent.

Hardly believing the results, I went back to the borstal in California where they had also recently finished the six-week supplement-taking period, and took a more detailed look at their records. I checked the incident report files for a full twelve weeks before and twelve weeks after the vitamin pills had first been issued. Yet again, there had been a very similar reduction in antisocial behaviour: this time it had dropped by thirty-seven per cent.

What could this mean? I now had two basic findings, discovered three years apart. First, the 1983 discovery: changing from a high- to a low-sugar diet produces about a forty per cent reduction in antisocial behaviour. Secondly, the 1986 discovery: giving vitamin and mineral supplements produces about a forty per cent reduction in antisocial behaviour. Obvious conclusion therefore: the extra vitamin and mineral content of the low-sugar diet was the key factor connected with the improvement in behaviour – the sugar content had nothing to do with it.

But I was still cautious. After all, my discovery that vitamin supplements can reduce violence in prisons was so revolutionary, and so against every known theory held by the experts in nutrition, psychology and criminology, that I hesitated to announce anything yet to the outside world.

I felt I needed to take things a stage further, and look at the issue from a slightly different angle. For example, I thought, if supplements can reduce antisocial behaviour, would they also perhaps reduce other negative aspects of the human psyche – like depression, anger, and stress?

I decided to give it a try, and gained the cooperation of a borstal just outside Miami in Florida – by the way, in case you're wondering why I had to do my research in so many different places, I had to make sure the results I was getting weren't due to something unique about one prison.

This time I didn't look so much at the children's

behaviour, but at their underlying psychological states. How did they feel? Were they happy, depressed, anxious, excitable, extravert, moody and so on? To help me to find out, I got hold of two of the standard tests routinely used by psychologists the world over (Profile of Mood States, and Minnesota Multiphasic Personality Inventory), and checked the kids out.

Perhaps you can guess the results, but I must say at the time they shook me.

I found that the children who showed the highest levels of negative emotions, like tension, depression, anger, fatigue and confusion, ate the worst diets, and responded the most to being given a vitamin and mineral supplement. The children who ate reasonably well didn't have anything like the same emotional problems, and didn't get so much benefit from the supplements.

This was just the kind of confirmation I needed. It meant that the improvements in the children's behaviour weren't some kind of odd-ball result – I now knew extra vitamins and minerals could produce lots of other psychological improvements, distinct in their own way, but obviously related to basic behaviour. The other thing it suggested was that extra vitamins and minerals weren't going to be of particular value to the children who were already eating a decent diet; if they already had enough nutrients from their food, giving them more didn't seem to have much effect.

The studies in Florida, California and Oklahoma gave me the second big breakthrough in my research. I was now confidently able to propose the following brand-new theory: *some antisocial behaviour in prisons is caused by malnutrition, and specifically by a lack of one or more vitamins and minerals.* The only thing I had to do now was actually to prove it! But you'll say: haven't you proved it already? What were all those studies you've just described to us all about?

Well the brutal fact is that those studies didn't prove anything; they were simply demonstrations that there *might* be a connection between malnutrition and behaviour. Why? Because of our old friends from Chapter 1 – the Experimenter, Hawthorne, Pygmalion and Placebo Effects. These are the arch-bugaboos of every experiment, the psychological gremlins that can hopelessly bias any results. You see, the children could well have been improving their behaviour because they were being given pills to swallow, and they knew how they were expected to behave. I know it sounds unlikely, but it's possible. And besides, I had to prove my theory to the thousands of my fellow scientists, the vast majority of whom I knew wouldn't believe a word of it. So I had to do an experiment that couldn't be criticised for having any psychological gremlins in it – it had to be flawless.

How could I do that? The answer was simple. I would pretend the vitamin supplements were a new drug, and test them in the same way that every new drug is tested.

If you think about it, every new drug given in hospital suffers from exactly the same psychological gremlins. If the attitude of the doctors and nurses is that the drug will work, that will probably influence how they view the patient's progress. Or if the patient himself thinks the drug's going to help him, it probably will. In fact there are hundreds of medical studies that show that if you give patients a pill with no drug in it at all, quite a few of them will get better completely spontaneously. This can sometimes be a very powerful effect indeed, and it is so common it's been called the placebo effect (from the Latin 'placebo', meaning I will please). By extension, the inert pill with no drug in it is called a placebo.

Fortunately the doctors and drug companies have discovered a way round the placebo effect. When they test a new drug, say a new headache pill, they round up about a hundred people who suffer from headaches, and ask them to help them test the pills. Unknown to the patients, however, half of them will not receive the new headache pill at all, but a fake pill (the placebo) that looks like, tastes like, and in every other way is totally like the headache pill – except that there's no drug in it. The crucial thing is that the patients must be unaware of whether they are getting the real or fake pill – they must be, in the jargon, 'blind'. But also, of course, it must be made impossible for anyone else involved in the experiment to bias the results. So everyone – the doctors, nurses, drug company staff and so on – have to be 'blind' too.

It all ends up as a rather complicated experiment: you need a secret code to identify the pills, you must make sure the patients are as alike as possible, and you must decide completely randomly who will get which pills. It's also got a rather complicated title – it's called a double-blind placebo-controlled trial – but it's the ultimate as far as experiments go, and if you want to prove a drug works beyond doubt, it's the only one that will cut the mustard.

Since what I was claiming was so controversial, I too had to prove it beyond doubt, so I had to submit it to the ultimate test – no one would believe me otherwise. I therefore set about organising a double-blind placebo-controlled trial.

It was, as they say, 'make or break' time.

Testing Behaviour and Mental Performance

But, because I was about to go to all this trouble, I thought to myself: as well as testing the malnutrition theory on anti-social behaviour, why not also try out the same theory on academic performance? After all, a million kids in New York had shown me that a better diet improved their school marks, and a million kids surely can't be wrong!

So I did a small preliminary experiment to see whether it would be worth while. A lot of scientists do this kind of thing – it's called a pilot experiment, and it's a sensible way of not wasting too much time and money barking up the wrong tree. Fortunately, also like a lot of scientists, I had a number of tame undergraduate students I could get to 'volunteer' to help me.

Because the New York children had gained better academic results after changing to a better diet, I wondered whether the root cause was that their basic mental performance had improved. Now, if that was the case, might it also not follow that people whose mental performance is good (i.e. are pretty bright) choose for themselves a better diet than people who are naturally less bright? To put it bluntly, might bright people be better nourished than dim people?

So I took a look at the students on my undergraduate courses, and picked out six who were the top academic performers. Then, at random, I chose fourteen others who were more middle-of-the-road. First I looked at what they ate, just as I had in the prisons, by controlling their food intake and measuring exactly what they ate and what they left.

I found that the six brightest students consistently ate a better diet – more fresh unprocessed food, and less junk. Now that might have been simply because the brighter ones knew how to eat better. But I doubted it: after all, the twenty students were pretty bright anyway (university students have IQs of at least 125), so there was no reason to suppose they didn't know the basics of good nutrition.

To check this out further, I did two things: I gave them all tests of intelligence (the standard kinds of IQ tests), and also asked them to give me samples of their blood. Analysing a person's blood is the best way of telling how well or badly nourished he or she is, because it gives you a precise measurement of the level of every vitamin and mineral in that person's body.

Again I found that the students with a higher IQ had higher levels of vitamins and minerals in their blood. So a connection between the two was beginning to look a liitle more likely. But of course, I still couldn't prove it – not yet anyway.

I decided to put both theories to the ultimate test – the behaviour theory and the one about mental performance – in one big properly controlled experiment. If it worked, all my theories would be vindicated. If it failed, I would have to go back to square one. It was now all or nothing, do or die, boom or bust.

By the spring of 1987, I had assembled an all-volunteer research team of nine people to help me conduct the first ever double-blind placebo-controlled trial of nutrition in any prison in the USA, and, as far as I am aware, the world.

This was going to be a very labour-intensive, very expensive, and very intrusive operation, and I knew I would have great difficulty in finding a prison that would agree to let me in. Fortunately, by that time, I had earned the respect of the Oklahoma Department of Human Services. They were sufficiently impressed that the level of violence and antisocial behaviour in their facility at Taft, Oklahoma had dropped by forty-three per cent within three days of starting the supplements, even though many of the prison staff had questioned the whole idea.

We decided to work with the seventy-one youths confined in the Central Oklahoma Juvenile Treatment Center (COJTC) near the capital, and the 140 inmates of the Lloyd E. Rader Center a hundred miles away near Tulsa. These were real juvenile delinquents, serving pretty long sentences for anything from armed robbery to rape and even murder.

Before starting the experiment proper, we did an enormous battery of tests. We gave each child a physical examination, a nutritional check-up by a registered dietician, we measured what each child ate for a week, and we took blood samples from all of them. In addition, twenty-six of the children agreed to take an IQ test. Then we gave them the vitamin and mineral pills.

Remember though, this time, half the children were randomly chosen to receive the real pills, and half identical-looking placebos that contained no nutrients at all. The secret code identifying which of them received the real ones was locked away – nobody had any idea who was getting what.

But, apart from taking a couple of pills a day, the children's routine was to continue as before. In particular, there was to be no change in the prison food. The pill-taking period was designed to run for three months. It began in April 1987.

Unfortunately, some of the prison staff, for reasons of their own, were not fully cooperative. Half way through the trial, we discovered that the Rader Detention Center began to fall down on giving the children their pills; in fact, none of the children at Rader ended up completing the full three-month course. I was naturally furious, but there was nothing I could do about it. It was a blow, because it meant 140 children had to drop out of the study. Nevertheless, it wasn't a total disaster. At COJTC, the other detention centre, the pill-taking was supervised not by the prison staff, but by nurses; the nurses were much more cooperative, and made sure that each of the seventy-one children got his daily tablets.

When the thirteen weeks were up, the prison governor at COJTC handed me the incident report records for the experimental period and for the three preceding months. I immediately saw an obvious difference: there had been a forty per cent drop in the number of offences. So something had happened, at least!

Nevertheless it was possible, and indeed likely, that there would have been a drop anyway because of the normal treatment programme within the prison. COJTC was a particularly enlightened detention centre, with a large staff of psychologists and counsellors. They had a good track record for rehabilitating offenders.

The critical question was: had the children on the real vitamin and mineral supplements done even better than the children who had taken the placebo tablets? And what about the IQ tests? Had the supplements had any effect there?

Finding the Proof

I retrieved the envelope containing the secret codes of the experiment, which had been kept for months under lock and key. I was now able to tell which children had been taking either the real or placebo supplements, and put them into two separate lists.

I went back to the incident report files, and totalled up the number of offences committed by the group of children on supplements, and compared it with the total number of offences in the placebo group (see fig 5). There was a very clear-cut difference. What was more there was a difference in the kinds of offences too. The more violent the bad behaviour, the more the improvement; for example, assaults on staff, the most serious offence of all, had dropped the most, whereas mere horseplay, for example, had dropped the least.

So the vitamins and minerals had worked! What was more, I was able to see exactly how much improvement each child had derived from taking the supplements. In fact, when I looked at their individual incident report records, I found that the largest reduction in offences had occurred in about one third of the children. They had shown massive improvements in behaviour of between seventy and ninety per cent!

I thought: I wonder if those children were the most malnourished? Fortunately, as you will remember, we had taken blood samples from the children – not just at the beginning of the experiment, but at the end as well. The blood gave us a perfect snapshot of every child's state of nutritional health. And sure enough, the blood analyses showed that the children who had the biggest improvements in behaviour were the ones who were originally malnourished in one or more vitamins and minerals. But by the end of the trial, the supplements had brought their levels of nutrition to normal.

What was more, the vitamins and minerals they had originally been deficient in were the very ones essential for the

fig 5

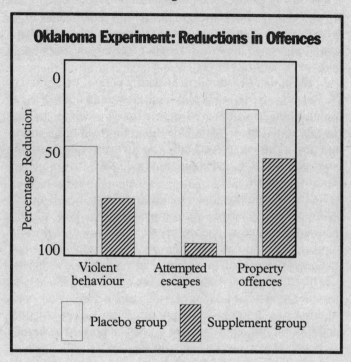

Oklahoma Experiment: Reductions in Offences

(Percentage Reduction)

0 — 50 — 100

Violent behaviour | Attempted escapes | Property offences

☐ Placebo group   ▨ Supplement group

chemical processes in the brain, and therefore crucial to proper brain function (see page 32 and fig 11, page 124).

So there we had it. First, I had established a connection between malnutrition and bad behaviour, conclusively demonstrated in the most rigorous kind of experiment known to science. Second, the date supported my theory that brain function is affected by marginal malnutrition.

I had my proof. But I wanted more.

If my theory that malnutrition affects brain function was correct, I wondered whether I could visibly demonstrate it by measuring actual changes in brain function in the children.

In fact, before the experiment started I had asked Oklahoma neurologist, Dr Barry Robbins, to test six of the worst-behaved children on his Brain Electrical Activity Mapping machine – the most advanced apparatus for studying brain function in the world. He confirmed to me that they all had abnormal brainwaves.

At the end of the supplement-taking period, we again sent Dr Robbins the same six children. He was amazed. Four of the children had improved dramatically; whereas the first time he tested them he had identified fourteen brain abnormalities, he now could find only two. In marked contrast, the other two children had eight abnormalities both before and after the experiment.

Neither Dr Robbins nor I had any idea which of the six children had received the supplements, and which the placebos. I looked up the secret codes, and saw that the four improved children had been the very ones on supplements, and that the two who hadn't improved had got the placebo tablets.

It fitted beautifully into place. We now had the final confirmation that what I had theorised years before – that brain function was limited by, among other things, the essential vitamins and minerals that are needed to power the brain's electrical system – was absolutely correct.

Having completed the study as far as the children's behaviour was concerned, next on my list was intelligence.

What about IQ?

I had recruited trained psychologists to give twenty-six of the children IQ tests before and after the thirteen-week supplement-taking period. I asked the psychologists to test two kinds of intelligence – so-called verbal IQ, and performance IQ (also called non-verbal intelligence).

I was obviously keen to see if there had been any gains in IQ scores as a result of taking the vitamins and minerals. First I looked at the differences between the children's verbal IQ scores, before and after. But not one of them had made any significant improvement. I then looked at the non-verbal test scores, and I found six of the children had improved dramatically: their IQ had shot up from between nine and twenty-five points! The rest of the children had gains of under nine points, but I couldn't claim that as a significant improvement as it might have been due to normal variation.

So I looked to see which tablets the top six had been taking, and I found that five of them had taken the real supplements, and only one the placebo. Furthermore, when I checked out their blood analyses, I found the same pattern as I had with behaviour: the children whose IQ had gone up the most had started out with the lowest levels of nutrients in their blood at the beginning of the experiment. They were obviously the ones most in need of the extra vitamins and minerals to bring their nutrient levels up to normal.

But why had one child improved his IQ score, and yet had not received the real supplements? The blood analyses gave us the clue: his nutrient levels had risen sharply during the experiment. How come? We questioned him, and discovered that he had voluntarily changed his eating habits; he had decided, all by himself, to give up eating the junk food he used to live on – like snacks and fizzy drinks – and eat much more of the good food on offer at the prison.

What had caused this sudden conversion? It emerged that he had been influenced by the dietician who had looked at him before the experiment. During her physical examination, she had found many physical signs of malnutrition in a fair number of the children – cracked and bleeding lips, bright red tongues, pale skin around the eyes and so on. She told the children that these were signs of specific nutritional deficiencies, and as any good dietician should, she advised them on how to clear those signs up. Apparently this motivated a few children to improve their eating habits.

This is a good illustration of the principle that if children are malnourished, they can improve their behaviour and IQ by either eating properly, or taking a supplement. Either will work. I shall return to this important topic at the end of the book.

The results of the study, of course, were very gratifying to me and my team. But they were also a bit of a bombshell for the prison officials.

The governor at COJTC, Roger Conway, was astounded: 'To be frank, initially I was sceptical. But we've now got kids who've stopped assaulting staff, they've stopped assaulting each other, they've stopped destroying property. It's clear we're going to have continue the vitamin programme.'

In fact the implications were clear for the whole state of Oklahoma. As Governor Henry Bellman put it: 'I would never have thought that providing adequate levels of vitamins and minerals would have this kind of an impact on someone's behaviour. This is a startling discovery, and if further tests substantiate what we've learnt so far, we will have to change the way we handle juvenile delinquents, and put much more emphasis on diet. But its greatest impact would be in our educational system. We already have a good school lunch programme, but if children, even when given access to good diets, don't consume all the food that's offered, we may need to find other ways of ensuring their nutrient requirements are met.'

It was a fitting tribute to my work.

4   The Welsh Experiment

Unknown to me, by one of those strange coincidences, a very similar experiment to ours in Oklahoma was going on 6000 miles away – at a school in North Wales.

The experiment was masterminded by Gwilym Roberts, the senior science master at Darland High School in Wrexham. He had become concerned about some disturbing changes he was noticing in his pupils. 'I've been teaching for thirty years now,' he told the BBC, 'and in the last eight years or so, I've found many more pupils lacking in concentration; they seem to have difficulty in following the lessons in class. They're either fidgety or irritable, or at the other extreme, very apathetic. And these are trends teachers have found right across Britain.'

Gwilym Roberts, like me, had no formal background in nutrition, but he had taken a keen interest in the subject to the extent of doing a three-year course at the Institute of Optimum Nutrition in London. It was there that he first heard about my own research on juvenile delinquents, and it struck a chord with him. He wondered whether the poor performance of some of the children at school might be related to what they were eating. He had a gut feeling that children's diets were changing for the worse.

So, like any good scientist in search of objective evidence, he made a detailed record of what nearly a hundred of his pupils ate over a three-day period. He was shocked: 'Some of them come to school with no breakfast, so in the morning they fill themselves up with crisps and confectionery from the corner shop. The same thing happens at breaktime and lunchtime.'

Part of the problem were the changes to the school-meals system in Britain. In the past, at midday, the vast majority of children had got at least one square meal provided free at school; it was a sensible public-health measure designed to ensure minimum levels of nutrition. But with the new Thatcherite policies, more schools were being officially encouraged to adopt optional cafeteria-style catering which children had to pay for – with predictable results. No marks for guessing that if children are able to decide what to eat, they don't always choose what's best for them nutritionally! In his mini-survey, Gwilym Roberts found something of a nutritional disaster area – the children who stayed at school for lunch often didn't buy the right foods, even though they were on offer. Worse still, some of them cut school lunch out altogether and headed for the local shops. And there was a worrying lack of concern from the parents: 'In the morning parents are usually rushing away to work, and have little time to give children breakfast – hence the fact that many of the children come to school on an empty stomach and fill up with confectionery – the foods we describe as the empty calories. And there has also been a general trend to eat more processed foods, the foods that look attractive and colourful, these are the ones children go for. Unfortunately, they are often not very nutritious.'

A Problem of Malnutrition

When Gwilym Roberts had the diets of his children analysed, they were found to be deficient in an *average* of ten vitamins and minerals recommended for children in America (as we shall see in Chapter 5, Britain doesn't have Recommended Daily Amounts for most of the micronutrients considered essential elsewhere in the world). Since an average always hides the best and the worst cases, some children had an absolutely appalling daily diet.

Some Typical Daily Diets

Q. 'What did you eat yesterday?'

SCHOOLGIRL AGED 12:

'I don't have breakfast because I don't have time usually. And it comes to dinner time and I have two sandwiches, packet of crisps, a chocolate biscuit, an apple, and maybe a glass of coke. And then usually – I go home from school and I get an ice-pop on the way home. And then I have jacket potato, pizza and beans for my dinner and I have swiss roll after it, with maybe a cup of coffee.

SCHOOLBOY AGED 11:

'For me breakfast, I had a drink of milk and a biscuit. I come to school. At the shop I had, um, a Mr Freeze, ice-pop, um, and at breaktime yesterday, I had a packet of crisps. At dinner time, I had chips, a bottle of milk, a packet of crisps, and a small packet of biscuits. And when I got home yesterday, I had bacon, sausage and egg and a drink of Tango orange drink, can, and an ice lolly and a packet of Polos. And that was what I had yesterday.'

SCHOOLGIRL AGED 11:

'In the morning I had a drink of tea with white sugar. Then for break I had a packet of crisps. And for my dinner I had, er, chips and, er, drink of Tango and a packet of crisps. Then for my tea, then I had chips.'

Having established that there was a malnutrition problem at his school, Mr Roberts wondered if theoretically this could be a possible cause of his pupils' poor classroom performance. A Bachelor of Science, he set about boning up on some of the latest research on the complex biochemistry of nutrition, and found, as I did, that micronutrients have a powerful role to play in brain chemistry. 'Many of these vitamins and minerals are involved in the enzymes which are absolutely essential for optimum brain function. So theoretically the dietary deficiencies we are seeing could well be affecting behaviour and performance.'

So in September 1986 he started an experiment to test whether giving vitamin and mineral supplements to his children might improve their performance and behaviour. It was designed very much like my own study in Oklahoma, with one group of children being given real tablets, another group dummy placebos, and a third group nothing at all. The children were also what is called 'pair-matched' for age, sex, academic ability, social class and so on. The trial was another classic double-blind placebo-controlled trial, the acme of scientific practice.

For the experiment, Gwilym Roberts enlisted the help of Dr David Benton, a psychologist from the University of Swansea; he offered to do a lot of the formal scientific work – for example, randomly allocating the real or fake tablets, and analysing the results. Dr Benton, by the way, was highly sceptical that the experiment would show anything at all, believing like the vast majority of experts that extra vitamins and minerals could not possibly affect someone's performance.

The study started with a group of ninety children being given a battery of mental tasks to test memory, concentration, and intelligence. Then they were given the supplements; some got the fake, some the real – nobody knew who got which.

After eight months on the tablets, the children were tested again, and their scores sent down to Dr David Benton at Swansea University. When he analysed them, he was at first unsurprised. There had been no significant change on either the memory or concentration tests. But when he looked closely at the IQ tests (see figs 6 and 7), something remarkable showed up. Whereas the children showed no difference in their scores on the verbal part of the IQ test, there was a

fig 6

Three Typical Non-Verbal IQ Tests

Decide how the first three figures are related and then find in the answer choices on the right the figure that belongs with them.

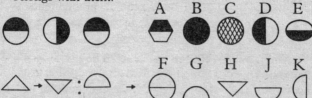

1 and 2 are related to each other: find the lettered figure that is related in the same way to 3.

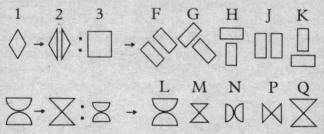

Find the Shape into which all three black pieces fit completely.

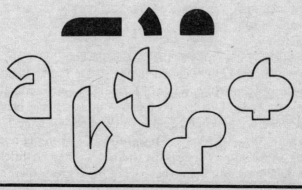

fig 7

Typical Verbal IQ Tests

Science deals with facts; it is wonderfully equipped to answer the question "How?", but it gets terribly confused when faced with the question "- - - - - - - - -"?

☐ *why*   ☐ *when*   ☐ *where*   ☐ *who*   ☐ *what*

A man in public office must expect to be the - - - - - - - for abuse.

☐ *target*   ☐ *enemy*   ☐ *basis*   ☐ *producer*   ☐ *source*

Which other word is in the same category as:

song   lecture   radio   opera ?

☐ *auditorium*   ☐ *sermon*   ☐ *theatre*
☐ *book*   ☐ *magazine*

lock   latch   catch ?

☐ *key*   ☐ *drawer*   ☐ *bolt*   ☐ *hinge*   ☐ *hide*

Methodist   Episcopal   Presbyterian ?

☐ *Buddhist*   ☐ *Atheist*   ☐ *Baptist*
☐ *Egotist*   ☐ *Pragmatist*

"Breeze" is to "hurricane" as "whisper" is to "- - - - - - - - - - - - "?

☐ *whine*   ☐ *murmur*   ☐ *sigh*   ☐ *sound*   ☐ *shout*

"Country" is to "prime minister" as "city" is to "- - - - - - - - - - "?

☐ *council*   ☐ *county*   ☐ *mayor*
☐ *town*   ☐ *capital*

considerable change in the non-verbal section. In fact, the children on the real supplements had registered an average gain of nine points in non-verbal IQ.

'I was astounded,' said Dr Benton when interviewed by the BBC for the *QED* programme. 'My expectation was that there would be no relationship between diet and intelligence. One is used to the idea that intellectual processes are influenced by social, cultural and genetic mechanisms. One doesn't doubt that severe malnutrition is going to influence intellectual functioning, but I had rather assumed people in

fig 8

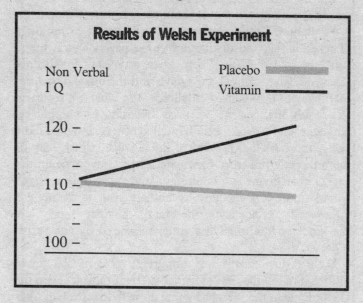

our Western society were by and large well nourished; so it is almost incredible to imagine that there could be very much variation in intelligence due to variations in nutrition. But the size of the change in IQ was quite phenomenal.'

It was the same result as the one I had obtained with the juvenile delinquents in Oklahoma. So, although Dr Benton and I had been working on two different continents, unaware of each other's existence, we had each made the identical discovery – a substantial increase in children's non-verbal IQ following the taking of vitamin and mineral supplements (see fig 8).

Unlike David Benton, however, I wasn't at all surprised. The study I had done with the million New York school-children, described in Chapter 2, had already suggested to me a link between diet and IQ; how else could one explain the rise in academic results after the authorities had improved the nutritional content of their school meals?

But the interesting thing about the new findings in 1988 was that only non-verbal IQ seemed to be affected. Why?

Dr Benton's view was very much the same as my own: 'There's a very old distinction in the psychological litera-ture', he told the BBC, 'between two types of intelligence – psychologists call one type *fluid*, and the other *crystallised* intelligence. Crystallised intelligence is what we've learnt as a result of experience at places like school – vocabulary, language and so on. Fluid intelligence is a much more basic, more biological kind of intelligence, which may be more directly linked to brain chemistry. So you would not expect that giving a vitamin and mineral supplement pill would improve someone's vocabulary, but it might well influence the efficiency of the brain's chemistry – precisely the kinds of fluid mental abilities measured by non-verbal IQ tests.'

We'll return to this very important topic in Chapter 8. Suffice it to say that by January 1988 two studies, one in the US and one in the UK, had come up with identical findings with some far-reaching implications. As David Benton put it: 'The implications are that there are a great number of children in our society who, if they were differently nour-ished, would be intellectually more capable.'

Vitamin Pill Fever

When he and I appeared on *QED* announcing our results to the programme's 10 million viewers, it caused a sensation.

'VITAMIN PILL FEVER – Parents in rush to boost children's IQ', announced the *Today* newspaper as front-page news. 'Chemists' shelves were left bare after claims that the tablets can improve youngsters' performance in tests.' According to the press reports, vitamin-pill manufacturers across Britain put their production lines into overdrive to cope with a sudden doubling of demand. Extra supplies were even apparently airlifted in from Europe. The BBC received hundreds of letters and phone calls, many from concerned teachers and parents who said the programme had confirmed their suspicions that poor nutrition might be connected with bad behaviour and declining academic standards. Most viewers also seemed to have got the other message of the programme that some children in Britain were in danger of being malnourished.

But the experts were not at all pleased. From them, there was virtually unanimous condemnation of the programme and the research findings it reported.

Their first objection was that people were going out and buying vitamin and mineral supplements. Parents were warned that vitamins can be dangerous. 'There's no way of controlling how much people buy in the shops,' London University nutritionist Dr Andrew Tomkin was reported as saying. 'If you give your child too many vitamins you may do more harm than good.' 'Cases have been reported of overdose from every vitamin,' trumpeted Professor Arnold Bender, 'with A and D the most common. . . . It is worth remembering that vitamin D is also used as a rat poison.' All very true, but the programme had not suggested giving megadoses of nutrients – and our experiments had been conducted with perfectly normal vitamin pills containing the regular quantities. In the Appendix (page 197) you'll see a list of the maximum-dose levels of all vitamins, that are generally considered not to cause any harm.

Another objection was that the programme had been transmitted two days before Dr Benton's findings were reported in *The Lancet*, thus depriving the scientific community of seeing the research data before the public. Scientists, you see, think themselves rather superior to ordinary people – they get miffed if they don't get to see scientific reports before the rest of you. Technically, *QED* was guilty of a minor breach of scientific etiquette, but it had been done with the full approval of both Dr Benton and myself.

In fact, the scientific community made a completely disproportionate fuss about this lapse of etiquette, despite the fact that the press regularly breach the so-called publication code with impunity – with premature cancer breakthroughs and the like. What the critics were doing of course was deploying the classic smokescreen technique. They were trying to divert attention from the real issues opened up by the programme. Why? Because it contained two Great Heresies.

Heresy No. 1 was the programme's suggestion that quite a few British schoolchildren were malnourished. London University Professor of Nutrition, Donald Naismith led that attack: 'In my opinion the majority of schoolchildren nowadays are well-nourished. There is a widely held view that young adolescents live entirely on things called junk foods. This is nonsense. There's no such thing as a junk food – anything that provides a child, or an adult for that matter, with energy is a food.' Senior Scientist at the prestigious Dunn Nutrition Unit in Cambridge, Dr David Thurnham, agreed: 'Children are getting a healthy diet. They may go through periods when perhaps they are not eating very much, but they are very, very unlikely to be malnourished. The public are being conned.'

The issue of malnutrition in Britain is an important one, and I shall be dealing with it in the next chapter.

But Heresy No. 2 was just as bad. For this the attack switched to Gwilym Roberts and David Benton, and their scientific report in *The Lancet*. They had claimed that their study of ninety children at Mr Roberts's school had shown that: a. a significant minority of children had a low intake of vitamins and minerals, and b. when thirty of them, randomly selected, received a supplement they had a nine-point increase in non-verbal IQ compared to the children on dummy tablets.

The editor of *The Lancet* was bombarded with letters from the nutritional establishment. They heaped scorn on Benton and Roberts, criticising the minutiae of their statistical analysis, condemning their nutritional survey, and questioning the ingredients of the supplement. Again, it was all a smokescreen designed to draw attention away from a finding none of them could bear to confront – that non-verbal IQ rose significantly in the children who had taken nutritional supplements. To orthodox nutritionists, the very idea was out of the question.

'This is the most scandalous paper I've seen printed in *The Lancet*,' Professor Yudkin told the press. 'The study is ludicrous, meaningless nonsense. They'll take a long time to live this down.' 'The dietary survey isn't worth the paper it's written on,' said Professor Naismith. 'I would be surprised if mental ability could be affected by diet.' The GPs weighed in too: 'Of all the amazing nutritional ideas, one of the craziest must be that extra vitamins can increase a child's intelligence', GP James le Fanu told the million readers of *The Daily Telegraph*.

The diatribes worked. Over the next weeks and months, most of the British press swallowed the line that the study could be ignored; it had been 'criticised' by scientists and so obviously it was all nonsense. Benton, Roberts, Schoenthaler and *QED* were to be 'castigated' for wilfully misleading parents and causing them unnecessary anxiety.

But some members of the establishment weren't quite so

sure. 'It's a revolutionary finding. I don't know what the truth is,' said Dr Roger Whitehead, head of the Dunn Nutrition Unit. But he explained why the nutritional establishment was so hostile. 'There may be a link between intelligence and malnutrition but only under circumstances where there is truly a deficiency. I think it would be very unlikely for the vast majority of the people in the United Kingdom that such a link exists. The diets of most people in the United Kingdom are so much greater than basic needs that such a link would be rare indeed. One would be talking about people whose dietary pattern was really quite bizarre. In the Third World, where the diet is very much worse than in the UK, it is much more easy to see that there could be impairment – the growth of brain cells could be affected. But in Britain, where our intake of nutrients is really very adequate, it is almost beyond belief to think that the current levels of consumption are inadequate for the brain cells to function properly.'

Dr Whitehead has very articulately put the issue in a nutshell.

In the next few chapters we shall be examining each element of the question. First, are people in Britain adequately nourished? Second, how strong is the scientific evidence that Western levels of malnutrition may affect brain function?

As we shall see, the issue is still controversial, but since the *QED* programme in January 1988 a lot more discoveries have been made. And most of them point in one direction.

References

Benton D., Roberts G., *Lancet* 23 Jan 1988, 140–143
Letters, *Lancet* 20 Feb 1988, 407–409

5 The Great British Diet

The Official View

Experts rarely agree on most things, but on the subject of the nutritional health of the Great British Public, there is remarkable unanimity.

First, this is what the government thinks: 'The standard of nutrition in Britain is generally good,' says one official DHSS document. Another one: 'The recommendations (about minimum nutritional standards in Britain) can be met by widely varying combinations of foods commonly consumed in the UK.' [DHSS. *Recommended intakes of nutrients for the UK*, HMSO 1969, 1981]

Secondly, the doctors: 'Diets in Britain already provide more than the present recommended intakes of most nutrients,' says *The British Medical Journal*, the mouthpiece of the medical profession. 'Nutritionists believe that with very few exceptions the diets of children in Britian contain enough vitamins to prevent deficiency diseases,' proclaims top paediatrician Leonard Taitz.

Now, the nutritionists: Starting at the top, here's Professor John Yudkin: 'Vitamins occur in the food we eat, and if we eat correctly we should – with very few exceptions – get all the vitamins we need. . . . Any sensible way of eating will give you these nutrients.' Fiona Hunter, spokeswoman for an organisation which represents most hospital and local authority dietiticians, gives their party line: 'The British Dietetic Association is of the opinion that if you eat a well-balanced and varied diet you should get all the vitamins and minerals you need. Certainly vitamins are lost when food is stored and processed, but not so much as to put us in danger from a shortage.'

In fact, most experts in nutrition – doctors, dieticians, professors, and government administrators – will generally give you the same story: food in Britain is so varied and nutritious that, if you eat normally, you will be properly nourished. And many of them also add: because practically everybody eats normally, there is nothing to worry about.

Reassuring, isn't it? It all sounds perfectly logical. And so it is. The problem is that it isn't true.

The crucial thing is that in order to decide whether someone is well nourished or badly nourished depends entirely on your definition of malnourishment. If I were to say, for example, that I was a good runner (which by the way I am not, as I am slightly to my shame overweight), I would be perfectly entitled to make that claim if the sporting authorities defined a good runner as somebody who could run a mile in twenty minutes. Now, that's not very fast – most people can *walk* a mile in that time! But if I lived in a country where the authorities said a twenty-minute mile was a good minimum standard of sports ability, I, along with virtually everyone else, would be classified as Runner Class 1.

For the authorities, it would be a sports utopia. Practically no one would need any extra training to help them achieve the national twenty-minute-mile minimum. No proper sports facilities would need to be built; any old bit of grass or dirt track would do to run on. Every now and again the authorities, being responsible guardians of the nation's sporting prowess, would need to review the situation; they would command a load of their experts to go out and test a random sample of a few thousand people to see how fast they could run. Years and millions of pounds later, the experts would report back to their paymasters. 'Everything's fine,' they would say. 'Nothing to worry about. There are a few who can't make twenty minutes, but it's only a few and they've probably got themselves to blame. Lazy good-for-nothings most of them. It's not a perfect world, anyway.'

Of course, any country which had a sports policy like that would be a joke – it would be the laughing-stock of the world, as well as a scandalous failure to its own citizens. But it's precisely how British governments have run their nutritional policy for the last forty years. Aided and abetted, of course, by the nutritionists and their RDAs.

Recommended Daily Amounts (RDAs)

It's the daily amounts of nutrients recommended by the British authorities that are the nutritional equivalent of the twenty-minute mile. Since the Second World War, successive governments have allowed the standards of minimum nutrition to remain at levels not tolerated in most other developed countries. In fact in Britain *for the majority of nutrients there are no standards at all*.

Part of the reason is historical. Once, British doctors led the world in setting standards of nutrition; they made some of the fundamental discoveries about deficiency diseases. The word 'Limey', for example, a term used to describe someone from Britain, came about because Dr James Lind, an eighteenth-century British nutritionist, discovered that scurvy could be cured by giving the patient citrus juice. Scurvy was a particular problem for seaman on long sea voyages, so he recommended that the Royal Navy give sailors limes or lemons to eat every day.

Dr Lind's lime ration was the world's first Recommended Daily Amount. We know now, of course, that the active ingredient in citrus fruit is a substance called Vitamin C. The term vitamin, by the way, was another British invention, coined in the 1920s. And during the early part of this century British nutritionists were world leaders in identifying the benefits of vitamins in preventing deficiency diseases like rickets (vitamin D), certain forms of blindness (vitamin A), beri-beri and pellagra (vitamin B).

The problem is that, although this is the latter part of the twentieth century, British nutritionists are still stuck on deficiency diseases. Meanwhile, the rest of the world's nutritionists have moved on. Take a look at the table below.

Recommended Daily Amounts of Vitamins*

	UK	USA	USSR	
A	750	1000	1500	(micrograms)
D	none	5	2.5	(micrograms)
E	none	10	15	(milligrams)
B1 (Thiamin)	1.2	1.4	1.7	(milligrams)
B2 (Riboflavin)	1.6	1.6	2.5	(milligrams)
B3 (Niacin)	18	18	19	(milligrams)
B6 (Pyridoxine)	none	1.8	2	(milligrams)
B12	none	2	2	(micrograms)
C	30	60	72	(milligrams)
K	none	75	250	(milligrams)
Folic acid	none	180	400	(micrograms)
Pantothenic acid	none	5.5	10	(milligrams)
Biotin	none	70	none	(micrograms)

*Average for male and female adults

Here you'll see a comparison between the Daily Amounts of vitamins Recommended in the USA, Britain and for good measure the Soviet Union. The first thing that strikes you is that out of the thirteen vitamins recommended in the USA and USSR, only five are recommended in the UK. Secondly, look at the individual figures: in Britain the RDAs of all vitamins are lower. Does this mean that people in America and Russia need more vitamins than Britons? Are they some kind of special beings? Of course not. What it means is that, elsewhere, nutritional experts have advised that their citizens will be healthy on those amounts, whereas the nutritional experts employed by the British government have advised that Britons will be healthy on much less. (In truth, I don't really know what advice British experts gave as I am not allowed to. It is all an Official Secret. So to be more accurate, let's just say that the experts did not publicly dissent when successive UK governments set Britain's RDA figures).

So how did this difference come about? It all boils down to attitude. Take the example of Vitamin C – UK RDA 30 milligrams, US RDA 60 milligrams.

When Vitamin C was first synthesised by chemists in the 1930s, it was discovered that the dose needed to cure scurvy was 10 milligrams a day. So when British nutritionists got their heads together to work out the RDA, the question they asked themselves was: 'What level of Vitamin C will well and truly prevent all known deficiency diseases due to lack of Vitamin C?' Since scurvy was the only disease they knew of, they reasoned as follows: 'If it's 10 mg to cure scurvy, then it's probably double that to prevent it, plus the same again to be on the safe side. Answer therefore: RDA = 30 mg.' Pure guesswork, and therefore not very scientific. But then the science of nutrition was not very advanced. (It's not much better now, but we'll come to that later.)

In the US there was a different attitude. Their nutritionists said to themselves: 'A deficiency disease like scurvy is the last stage of collapse of an organism, so it's likely that other more minor symptoms occur way before the final disease strikes. Let's not therefore just prevent scurvy, let's try and get people as healthy as possible so that the body is functioning as optimally as possible.'

Totally different attitude: totally different RDA. It's the same story with the minerals.

Minerals – some of which are also called trace elements – are just as important as the vitamins to our health. Many of them are in fact fundamental to our very existence, as they are directly involved in the complex chemical reactions that take place every microsecond in the billions of cells in our bodies. If, for example, your body didn't contain a trace of zinc, virtually all your cells would pack up. Instant curtains.

Recommended Daily Amounts of Minerals*		UK	USA	USSR
Calcium	(mg)	500	800	800
Phosphorus	(mg)	none	800	1600
Magnesium	(mg)	none	320	500
Iron	(mg)	10	12.5	17
Iodine	(mcg)	none	150	150
Zinc	(mg)	none	13.5	17
Chloride	(mg)	none	750	5000
Sodium	(mg)	none	500	5000
Potassium	(mg)	none	2000	3750
Fluoride	(mg)	none	2.75	0.75
Copper	(mg)	none	2.5	2.5
Manganese	(mg)	none	3.75	7.5
Selenium	(mcg)	none	65	none
Chromium	(mcg)	none	125	none
Cobalt		none	none	none
Silica		none	none	none
Vanadium		none	none	none
Nickel		none	none	none
Molybdenum		none	none	none

*Average for male and female adults

Above are listed all the minerals that are known to be absolutely necessary to human beings, the so-called Essential Minerals. Compare again the RDAs in the USA, USSR and Britain. Of the nineteen essential minerals, twelve have recommended daily intakes in the USSR, fourteen in the USA, but only two in Britain.

So, if you add the vitamins, a grand total of twenty nutrients scheduled in the USA are ignored in Britain. Why? Again, it's the British attitude, summed up in the latest official DHSS publication on RDAs:

> Deficiency of these vitamins and minerals is either rare, or associated with certain medical conditions, or has not been described or confirmed in man in the United Kingdom. With the exception of vitamin B12, which is found almost entirely in foods of animal origin, these nutrients occur in sufficient quantity in a large number of foods. Therefore in the light of present knowledge and in the context of the United Kingdom diet, recommended amounts for these nutrients have not been set. [*Recommended Daily Amounts of food energy and nutrients for groups of people in the United Kingdom* HMSO 1988].

Simple logic: no known deficiency = no problem = no RDA. It's the bare minimum, twenty-minute-mile approach. And besides, as we shall now see, it's not even true; for there *are* deficiencies in Britain of quite a few nutrients that don't have British RDAs, and even of some that do.

The Diets of British Schoolchildren

Let's take a look at an official survey of the state of nutrition in Britain. As it happens, one of the most recent is central to the topic of this book, as it concerns the eating habits of children. In 1989 the Department of Health published *The Diets of British Schoolchildren*, a massive 300-page document that took almost a decade to produce, and which must have cost at least a million pounds.

First, some background. One of the first things Margaret Thatcher did after she came to power was to abolish the free compulsory school meal. Under the 1980 Education Act local authorities no longer had to provide a midday meal, and, if they did, it did not have to meet any minimum nutritional standards. The children from poor families were excepted, but not for long. Six years later their free school meal was abolished too.

To say the least, it was not a popular move, even among the government supporters. Two so-called Conservative wets were somewhat concerned, but to allay their fears an in-depth study was promised that would monitor the effects of the new legislation. *The Diets of British Schoolchildren* is the result.

When the report was published in 1989, the Minister of Health, David Mellor, gave the press the predictable official line: 'This is a highly detailed scientific analysis. . . . It shows that schoolchildren in all social classes were well nourished and thriving. . . . All of them had adequate, or more than adequate intakes of nutrients.'

Unfortunately, the Minister was, to put it at its least impolite, somewhat badly advised. Read the report and it actually says nothing of the sort. In fact what it says is pretty alarming; what it tends to obscure is even worse.

Over 3000 children (boys and girls aged ten to eleven, and fourteen to fifteen) were surveyed across the country, and they were each monitored for a week to see what they ate. This is what the report found: 'All the children consumed large quantities of bread, cakes, biscuits, puddings, milk, meat products, crisps, potatoes and particularly large quantities of chips. . . . Older children ate more chips, white bread and poultry and drank more tea than younger children while these in turn ate more puddings and drank more fizzy drinks.'

This is what the report said about the effect of the loss of the school meal: 'Older children, especially girls, who ate out of school at places such as cafés, take-away or "fast food" outlets chose meals which were low in many nutrients, particularly iron. . . . The overall nutritional quality of their diet was the poorest of [all].'

Fast foods, take-aways, cakes, meat products, chips, chips and chips does not represent the kind of diet any layman would imagine was normal, healthy, or well balanced. And yet the experts involved in the survey were not at all dismayed. Dr Roger Whitehead was a senior member of the report's scientific panel: 'You've got to be very careful', he told the BBC 'about making generalisations about these foods being inadequate in nutrient intake. They may not be the best balance, they may not be the best for instance in the proportion of fat in them, but when you add up all the nutrients that have been consumed during the course of the day from fast foods, from convenience foods, it's remarkable how normal the overall pattern can be.'

Indeed. According to the report, most children eating these kinds of foods were perfectly OK nutritionally. The government researchers worked out their intakes of the macronutrients, fat protein and carbohydrate, and they concluded the children were eating well enough; after all, they all seemed to be putting on weight and height satisfactorily. But when it came to the micronutrients, things weren't quite so rosy: the older girls had iron, calcium and riboflavin levels below the RDAs. To the layman, that sounds fairly serious, but the report brushed any concerns aside. On iron: 'The clinical significance of these [below RDA] intakes is not clear without further studies of iron status.' On riboflavin: 'Riboflavin deficiency is not seen in Great Britain and without further biochemical data it is difficult to assess whether these dietary findings have any clinical significance.' On the low calcium RDAs, the report made no comment.

So the British nutritionists were able to say that, with a few rare and probably unimportant exceptions, kids in Britain are officially well nourished. But what would the same report look like if it had been done in the US? Look at the table on the next page, taken from *The Diets of British Schoolchildren*.

You'll see that if the report had been done in the US, their experts would have been far more concerned about the

Are British Children Well Nourished?

BRITISH CHILDREN AGED 10 TO 11

Average intake	Boys	Girls	UK RDA*	US RDA*
Calcium (mg)	833	702	700	1000
Iron (mg)	10	8.6	12	13
Thiamin (B1) (mg)	1.2	1.0	0.9	1.2
Riboflavin (B2) (mg)	1.7	1.4	1.2	1.3
Niacin (mg)	26.5	23.1	14	16
Vitamin C (mg)	49.3	49	25	47.5
Vitamin A (mcg)	854	691	575	850
Vitamin D (mcg)	1.48	1.32	none	10
Vitamin B6 (mg)	1.17	1.03	none	1.6

BRITISH CHILDREN AGED 14 TO 15

	Boys	Girls	UK RDA*	US RDA*
Calcium (mg)	925	692	700	1200
Iron (mg)	12.2	9.3	12	13.5
B1 (mg)	1.47	1.04	1	1.3
B2 (mg)	1.9	1.3	1.5	1.5
Niacin (mg)	32.6	24	19	16.5
C (mg)	49.3	48	30	50
Vitamin A (mcg)	969	801	740	900
D (mcg)	1.63	1.24	none	10
B6 (mg)	1.35	1.06	none	1.8

(*Average values)

children. They would have found deficiencies across the board in calcium, iron, vitamins A, D, and B6, and borderline deficiencies in vitamin C and riboflavin – not to mention any other possible deficiencies in nutrients like zinc, selenium, and the rest of the minerals for which the British government has no RDAs and which therefore the survey conveniently ignored.

The UK experts do make a passing reference to the US

RDAs – on the one item, vitamin B6. 'Average intakes were below [the US RDA] but there is no evidence of B6 deficiency in Britain.' (There we go again: no deficiency = no problem = no RDA. And of course the converse works beautifully too: no RDA = no problem). Remember too that 'no evidence' does not mean a deficiency doesn't exist; it just means they haven't found one – they may well not have looked. Some depressions and anxiety states for example have been linked to lack of B6 – couldn't they be classified as a deficiency disease? Again, it's a question of attitude. In Britain, nutritionists simply don't recognise any B6 deficiency, period. (That's why, when you go to your doctor suffering from anxiety, he'll probably diagnose you as having a Valium deficiency!)

British nutritionists, when challenged with the US RDA levels, often dismiss them as being needlessly high. For example, the Benton and Roberts study on the Welsh schoolchildren was heavily criticised for daring to use the US RDAs in preference to the UK ones, and gave the British nutritional establishment another excuse, as you say in Britain, to 'pooh-pooh' the findings. Their argument is that the British food supply and eating habits are so different from those in America that the two countries cannot be compared. 'It's just not cricket,' they say, 'to criticise one chap's nutrition with another chap's RDAs.'

OK. Let's be scrupulously fair to the British nutritionists, and assume that their RDAs are totally right, and everyone else's are off the wall. On that basis, we'll now take a closer look at *The Diets of British Schoolchildren*, the government's own latest in-depth report on the nutritional health of Britain's 8½ million schoolchildren, published in 1989.

You may remember that on page 82 we said the report showed that, with a few exceptions in girls, British schoolchildren were adequately nourished. Well, that wasn't, strictly speaking, true. Oh yes, the official line is that the report does indeed show that – but in fact it doesn't.

fig 9

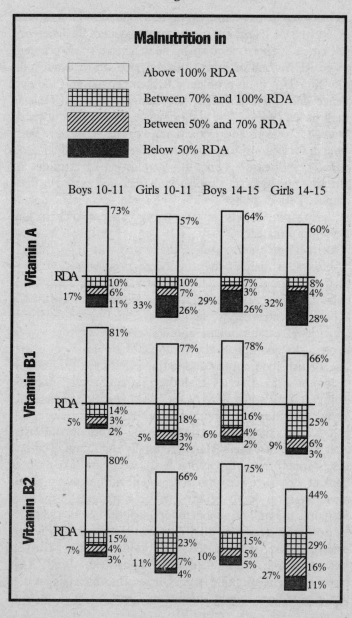

fig 9a

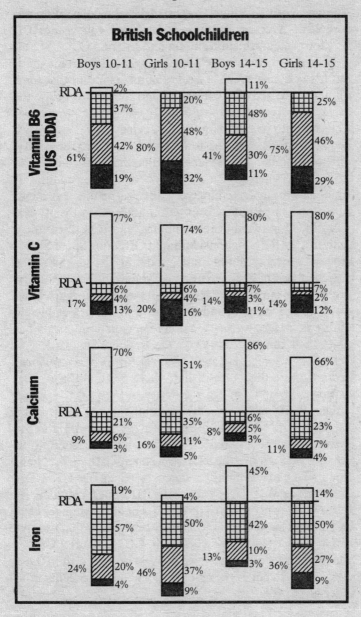

The most positive claim the report makes about the children as a whole is: 'Average . . . nutrient intakes were above the RDA . . . for protein, thiamin, niacin and Vitamin C'.

Note the word 'average'. A seemingly unimportant word, but it's not: an average of a set of numbers means that some numbers are above the average, and others are below the average. An average can be used to conceal a lot of information. Let's take our twenty-minute-mile analogy. Say there are five people who are reported to be able to run an average of a nineteen-minute mile, what could that mean? It could mean that each person really can run it in about nineteen minutes. It could also mean something very different: Runner A might run it in four minutes, B in ten minutes, C in twenty-one minutes, D in twenty-seven minutes, and E in thirty-three minutes. So, if the National Minimum Running Speed Standard was a twenty-minute mile, and you just looked at the average speed of nineteen minutes, you would say 'Great, no problem, all our runners are OK'. But look at the figures that make up the average, and the picture would be completely different. 'Heck, we've got a problem,' you'd say. 'Sixty per cent of our runners can't make the National Standard.'

Let's now look again at *The Diets of British Schoolchildren*, and scrutinise the figures behind those bland averages. The findings are shown in figs 9 and 9a.

The charts are less complicated than they look. Take Vitamin A, for example. Remember that, according to the British Government report, all the children achieved an average intake above the RDA. So, superficially no problem. But in fact many children failed to reach the UK RDA standard. Look at the box above the RDA line for Vitamin A. It shows that only seventy-three per cent of the younger boys had intakes higher than the RDA, which means that twenty-seven per cent didn't achieve the RDA figure. Of the younger girls forty-three per cent were below the RDA, thirty-six per cent of the older boys and forty per cent of the older girls.

Look through the rest of the nutrient charts, and you'll see that a staggeringly high percentage of the children failed to meet the basic nutritional standard. And remember these figures are all based on the UK government's own RDAs, which are already among the lowest in the world.

Given such large percentages of apparently malnourished children, how come none of the experts seem to be bothered by it? The answer is because of the rather strange way in which nutritionists have constructed the RDA system to work.

When you read on your cornflake packet that a 100 gram serving will give you, say, thirty per cent of the RDA of thiamin, most people imagine it means what it says; i.e., eat three and a bit servings, and you've got your daily thiamin fix. However, strictly speaking, that's not true. According to the nutritionists, the RDA does not refer to individuals, but to groups of people – a kind of group average.

In *The Diets of British Schoolchildren* report, the authors thoughtfully provide the following explanation:

> The RDAs are estimated so that the requirements of almost all members of a group of healthy people are met. Consequently they are higher than average *requirements* [their italic]. In practice if the *average* intake of a nutrient is at or above the RDA it can be assumed that the requirements of almost all individuals have been met. While in any group there may be individuals with nutrient intakes below the RDA, this does not necessarily imply dietary deficiency, which can be established only by clinical and biochemical tests of nutritional status.

Ah ha! So the RDA is not a minimum requirement at all, it's way above. That means there's even more reason why we shouldn't have anything to worry about. All those enormous percentages of children with intakes below the RDA are perfectly all right. What a relief.

But wait . . . if the RDA is not the minimum requirement,

what is? It's here that some nutritionists say 'pass'; they invoke the letter of the RDA system, and repeat: 'We can only tell you about group averages and not individuals'. It sounds like a cop-out, and it is. They're so concerned about scientific exactitude that they end up not being able to say very much about anything.

But most nutritionists, I am glad to say, do live in the real world. Despite the arcane RDA system, they do permit it to be used to extract some information at least about individuals and their nutritional status. They have an informal rule-of-thumb measure of dietary deficiency which says that if someone is receiving less than seventy per cent of the RDA of any nutrient, that person is likely to be malnourished.

So let's rule our thumbs once more down those charts on pp. 86–87. Look again at Vitamin A intake: the chart shows that seventeen per cent of the younger boys, thirty-three per cent of the younger girls, twenty-nine per cent of the older boys, and thirty-two per cent of the older girls had intakes below seventy per cent of the RDA. In other words, getting on for a third of all children in Britain are likely to be lacking Vitamin A.

Look at the rest of the nutrients: Vitamin B1 doesn't seem too bad – only between five and nine per cent of children are likely to be malnourished. But let's translate that into real numbers. There are 8.5 million schoolchildren in Britain, so every one per cent represents 85 000 individuals. That means about 1 million children are probably deficient in Vitamin B1.

Vitamin A: over 2 million deficient children
Vitamin B2: about 1 million
Vitamin C: about 1.5 million
Calcium: about 1 million
Iron: nearly 2.5 million
Vitamin B6: if these were American children, and therefore we applied the US RDAs, there are a staggering 5.5 million British children deficient in B6.

Just in case there are any real hard nut(ritionist)s out

there, I've also included the percentages of children whose nutrient intakes were *below half* the RDA level. Even a hard nut should recognise that someone getting less than fifty per cent of the RDA might have a serious malnutrition problem.

So we are talking about literally millions of children in Britain being seriously malnourished . . . and remember, malnourished On Her Majesty's Government's own figures.

There's ample supporting evidence for this very worrying conclusion from other surveys, both public and private, large and small. Not many organisations have the resources of the government, but Taylor Nelson is one of the few that do. They do regular assessments of the eating habits of their Family Food Panel, a vast survey of 5500 families across Britain. Their aim is to report on changing consumption patterns for the benefit of the food manufacturing industry, so that the manufacturers can 'target' new products more effectively. One study of theirs in 1989 called *Kid's Stuff – an Analysis of Children's Eating Habits* revealed just how soft a target children in Britain really are. Since their previous report in 1985, Taylor Nelson today find that the amount of vegetables and fresh fruit eaten by children has dropped by up to a third, while consumption of convenience foods has risen – crisps, packet desserts, biscuits, tinned pasta, take-aways, sausages, burgers and the rest of the familiar dismal litany. In addition, as Welsh schoolmaster Gwilym Roberts had observed, more and more children are going to school without any breakfast.

Lack of breakfast was also reported in another recent survey, published by the Health Promotion Research Trust, of a random sample of over 9000 British adults. In the eighteen to thirty-nine-year-old age group, over thirty-five per cent never had breakfast, while in contrast nearly fifty per cent of them ate fried food and chips every day. And did you know that an average of two thirds of the British population never eat salad in the winter?

A 1983 study on the sugar intake of 400 British schoolchildren found that sugar-rich 'snacking' was 'the major component of their eating habits', and that only five per cent of their sugar consumption came from fruit. By contrast, in a tiny research project, Bristol GP Dr John James did blood tests on children under four to check for iron status – and found that one child in six was deficient.

Bristol is also the headquarters of the Early Childhood Development Unit, a private foundation which for the last fifteen years has been pioneering intervention projects in the community. Its director Dr Walter Barker is particularly keen on nutrition, and he has developed a series of imaginative self-help advice packages to encourage parents to improve their children's diets. And they certainly needed encouragement; when he and his team did a survey of families with three- to four-year-old children in South Wales, this is the kind of thing they found:

Some Typical daily diets of 3–4 year-olds in South Wales

AVERAGE CHILD

8.20	a.m.	tea; digestive biscuit
10.00	a.m.	milky coffee; 1 slice toast; margarine
12.30	p.m.	1 egg sandwich (white); crisps
3.00	p.m.	coffee; biscuit
4.00	p.m.	sausage; chips; tea
6.00	p.m.	sweets

WORSE THAN AVERAGE CHILD

7.30	a.m.	cola
9.00	a.m.	cream biscuit
12.00	p.m.	cheese and onion pastie; chips; milky coffee
3.00	p.m.	sweets
4.00	p.m.	crisps
5.00	p.m.	pop
6.00	p.m.	8 ozs milk

Walter Barker and his team also did a much larger study on over 200 younger children between the ages of three months and two and a quarter years, precisely recording what they ate over a four-day period, and then analysing the results for nutrient intake. Using the seventy per cent RDA benchmark, they found roughly half the children deficient in folic acid, vitamin B6, vitamin C, and iron, two-thirds deficient in zinc, vitamin D and vitamin E, and all of them deficient in magnesium.

'One of the most disturbing things about our findings,' says Dr Barker, 'is that as the children got older, and switched to a more adult-type diet, their nutrient intake dropped significantly. By the time they were eighteen months old they were eating very much like their parents – processed meat products, white bread, sugar, sweets, chocolates, biscuits, cereals, soups, fizzy drinks and squash; they had very little fruit, vegetables or fresh meat.' Because his staff travel widely in Britain, visiting hundreds of families a week to teach them preventive health, he is able to get a good overview of the state of the nation.

There really is a serious problem in Britain that the government isn't addressing; there is a great deal of marginal as well as more serious malnutrition particularly in disadvantaged areas of the country. Poor families find it difficult to afford to buy proper food, and also they lack the education to know what to buy. The expert nutritionists employed by the government are blind to a lot of this. All they seem to be concerned about are the macronutrients like energy and protein; if those are all right, then they don't see a problem. But it's a crude third world kind of attitude. They ought to care about all the micronutrients, the vitamins and minerals, some of which are very low indeed. The only one they seem to fasten on is iron; well, I suppose they need to have one honorary micronutrient to worry about.

At the beginning of this chapter, I said that the official British government line has always tended to be that the British eat reasonably well, and that with some rare exceptions, people have no serious nutrient deficiencies. This is the Gospel According to Nutritionists on High, but as we have seen, to put it in the politest way possible, it is nothing but wishful thinking.

But Those on High may not all be guilty of self-delusion; some of them may know precisely what they are doing. The fact is that deciding on the RDAs of vitamins and minerals is not entirely a nutritional matter – it's also highly political. The levels of RDAs have enormous commercial and financial implications.

Going back to our twenty-minute-mile analogy; if the minimum standard were suddenly changed to a ten-minute mile, then probably half the population would fail. Think of the money that would then have to be spent on extra training, sports facilities and so on.

As we have seen, it's only because the RDAs are so low or non-existent that Britain's nutritional problem remains hidden. If the UK were to bring the RDA levels up to the US standards, the true state of malnutrition would be revealed, and that in turn would generate at least two major consequences: 1. The highly processed manufactured foods which form the basis of the average British diet could no longer be claimed to be adequate. 2. The levels of social security payments to the poor would have to be considerably increased to enable them to afford better food.

Let's take the social security issue first. It's been estimated that there are over 4 million children in Britain living near the poverty line and eligible for some form of Supplementary Benefit. Tim Lobstein of the London Food Commission has managed to unearth what the DHSS presumes poor families need to spend on food (see opposite).

Horrifying. Given the relative costs of foods, and the paltry sums officially allowed for food purchases, it's hardly

Calorific Content and Supplementary Benefit

FAMILIES ON SUPPLEMENTARY BENEFIT; PRESUMED SPENDING
ON FOOD (1986/7)

Adult	£1.61	per day
Child 16–17	£0.79	„
Child 11–15	£0.63	„
Child 0–11	£0.43	„

DHSS RECOMMENDED MINIMUM ENERGY REQUIREMENTS PER
DAY

	Calories	Benefit per 100 calories
Adult	2700	6.0p
Child 16–17	2500	3.2p
Child 11–15	2400	2.6p
Child 6–10	1950	2.2p
Child 3–5	1550	2.8p

COST OF 100 CALORIES FROM DIFFERENT FOODS

Tomatoes	70p	Crisps	9p
Cod fillet	50p	Mars bar	8p
Lean beef	40p	Meat pies	7p
Oranges	25p	Potatoes	6p
Lean pork	23p	Chips	6p
Fruit juice	20p	Sausages	6p
Chicken leg	18p	Wholemeal bread	3p
Cola drink	16p	White bread	2p
Cabbage	15p	Sugar	2p
Apples	14p	Lard	1p

surprising that poor parents choose to feed their children the
foods that give the most value-for-money calories. Neither is
it surprising that children, left to their own devices, will do
the same. Unfortunately, as the list shows all too clearly, the
most cost-effective foods tend to be the very ones with the
lowest nutritional value.

So it follows that the British government would have to think twice about making the RDA levels any higher than they are, for fear of exposing the real malnutrition in their midst.

A higher set of RDAs would also hit the food manufacturers. Their highly processed foods are already low enough in vitamins and minerals as it is, what with the losses due to processing, and the fact that the basic ingredients are often so poor nutritionally. The manufacturers therefore would no longer be able to get away with supplying the pies-burgers-fizzy drinks-savoury snacks-sugary snacks-chips-chips-chips mish-mash that is the Staple British Diet; it would be shown up as the nutritional wasteland it really is.

In fact, at present, the British government is currently considering a wholesale revision of the nation's RDAs. A committee headed by Dr Roger Whitehead has spent the last two years agonising over whether Britain can continue to justify its low RDA standards. Its conclusions (which are awaited in spring 1991) will depend crucially on the attitude of the nutritionists on the panel. Will they continue with the old twenty-minute-mile mentality, and tinker about with RDA figures at the margins of malnutrition? Or will the nutritionists change the habits of a lifetime and grasp the opportunity of radically altering their whole philosophy – from the twenty-minute mile bare minimum to *optimum* nutrition?

However, whichever approach they take, there are some revolutionary new findings they are going to have to take account of. These are the subject of the next few chapters.

References

DHSS, *Prevention and Health*, HMSO 1977.
Passmore, R. et al., *BMJ* 1979, 1: 527–531.
Taitz L., *BMJ* 25 June 1988, 1753.
The A to Z of Slimming, John Yudkin.

The Diets of British Schoolchildren, HMSO 1989.

Cox, B. D. et al., Health & Lifestyle Survey, Cambridge University School of Clinical Medicine.

Hackett, A. F., et al, Brit. J. Nutr *British Journal of Nutrition* 1984, 51, 347–356.

James J., J. Roy. Coll. GPs, Aug 1988.

Lobstein, T. *Poor Children Poor Diet*, Childright July 1989.

6   The QED Catalyst

When the *QED* programme 'Your Child's Diet on Trial' was broadcast in January 1988, it certainly started something – not just among the general public, but among the whole nutritional establishment.

As I described in Chapter 4, most of the reaction among scientists was hostile – the programme questioned too many orthodoxies in too many academic fields for it to have a cat in hell's chance of being anything but unwelcome. So while some members of the Empire Struck Back, most of them simply ignored it.

But there were just a few who weren't quite so dismissive. They thought that what the programme reported was important enough to be taken seriously, and with such a large public response they felt impelled to act. Dr Roger Whitehead was one of the first to see its importance: 'Unlike many of my colleagues I felt that one couldn't dismiss the issue.' he told the BBC.

For one thing it had a great deal of publicity, everyone was talking about it, and I decided we just can't leave it there, we really had to go and see whether this finding is true. After all, the link between diet and intelligence is one of the most important issues of the lot – probably *the* most important consequence of dietary manipulation one can imagine. Man is a thinking animal, man survives because of his ability to think, and if something in the diet is interfering with that ability to think, then that is very detrimental indeed. It's arguably much more important than the link between diet and cardiovascular disease, for example, which only affects half the population. Anything which affects thought affects the whole of the population. So, very soon after the programme when I was telephoned by the Department of Health for my views, I told them we had better repeat the study to see what the findings are.

So Dr Whitehead set up a special committee under the auspices of the Medical Research Council to plan a further study – not a large one, but a small pilot study costing a few thousand pounds. But he was beaten to it. A group of community health scientists in Scotland had already been given £30 000 by the Scottish Hospitals Endowment Research Trust for an identical study of their own. So the MRC decided to take a back seat.

The Scottish project was headed by Professor Charles Florey of the Department of Community Medicine at the University of Dundee: 'Our initial reaction to the QED report was what most people felt – one of disbelief,' he admitted. 'It seemed biologically so unlikely that a small dietary intervention could have such a profound effect on intelligence. But it was potentially of great public health importance, and if it were true then we would have to look very seriously at the diet of the nation's children.'

Thus he and three colleagues set about doing a carbon copy of the experiment David Benton and Gwilym Roberts had done with the Welsh schoolchildren. They got the agreement of over eighty eleven to thirteen year olds at a local school, and in September 1988 started giving vitamin and mineral supplements to half the children, and fake placebo tablets to the rest.

Meanwhile in London, Professor Donald Naismith had just completed a hastily mounted experiment of his own. He was one of the original sceptics who had publicly condemned the whole idea. He told the BBC: 'The notion that learning ability in children could be influenced by diet, in a community like the United Kingdom, seemed so highly improbable that its publication in a prestigious medical journal like *The Lancet* was a matter of deep concern to many nutritional scientists. Nevertheless we decided that the whole question was too important to leave as it was.' He and his team found a school in London, and gave supplements and placebos to over 150 schoolchildren for four weeks, testing their IQ before and afterwards.

But they found absolutely nothing; the pills had not the slightest effect. 'It is clear that no improvement in intellectual performance can be expected from vitamin and mineral supplements,' Professor Naismith and his colleagues at King's College announced unhesitatingly.

But it was now their turn to be criticised. 'I was very surprised at their unequivocal conclusions,' wrote David Benton. 'Rarely if ever does a single study prove or disprove a hypothesis; scientists should not suggest otherwise.' Dr Rippere of the Institute of Psychiatry also slammed them for having given the supplements over too short a period. 'It cannot be assumed that complex mental processes involved in IQ test performance will improve so quickly.'

In addition, some criticised the Naismith experiment as not being a proper replication of the Welsh experiment. So the results of the study in Scotland were eagerly anticipated, not least by Dr Roger Whitehead's committee at the Medical Research Council. 'I should be very surprised indeed if the Scottish study produces the same results as the Welsh study, but if it does, it really will put the cat among the pigeons nutritionally speaking. We would then have to start thinking about much bigger studies, perhaps the biggest nutritional study that has ever been carried out in the UK. It's that important.'

The Scottish children finished taking the tablets at the end of the school year in June 1989, but it took a further nine months before the results were published. Again *The Lancet* announced their conclusions, once again with supreme confidence: 'Vitamin and mineral supplementation does not improve the performance of schoolchildren in tests of reasoning.' But looking closely at their data, it emerged that this oh-so-firm statement wasn't entirely justified, and that they had in fact found something: the children who had been given the supplements did score more highly on two of the non-verbal tests – raising their IQ by an average of two and a half points. On three other non-verbal tests, however, there was no improvement at all. The experiment was not what scientists call 'statistically significant'; in other words, it was possible that these small increases in IQ had occurred by coincidence, and had nothing to do with the supplements at all.

My own explanation of why this study in Scotland showed such a weak increase in non-verbal IQ is because the Dundee schoolchildren were not that malnourished in the first place. In fact only four children were considered to be seriously deficient, and that's far too few to show any global effect. Remember, as all my experiments in the US have shown, if you already have a good diet and you're not malnourished, then no amount of extra vitamins and minerals is going to significantly improve your behaviour or intelligence.

By coincidence, at the same time as the Scottish study, came the announcement of the results of a similar investigation in Belgium. This one had been done on over 160 thirteen-year-olds by a Brussels University paediatrician, Dr Jean-Paul Buts, in conjunction with Dr David Benton of Swansea University – remember, he had done the original experiment with the Welsh schoolchildren. This time, they found very clear evidence that supplements did have an effect, with over an eight-point difference in non-verbal IQ between the children taking the tablets and those not – but only for the most malnourished children; the relatively well-nourished children showed no major difference in IQ scores.

But Drs Buts and Benton found something rather strange.

The children who had a poor diet and who did not take the extra vitamins and minerals performed *worse* the second time they took the IQ test. It was as if they were bored with the whole thing, and couldn't be bothered to try the second time around. David Benton concludes that what may be happening is that the supplements are not actually increasing IQ *per se*, but preventing it from falling. He thinks that a poor diet makes children inattentive and produces a bad attitude to work, and that supplements can correct that.

What David's saying chimes in very much with my own views and findings over the last ten years: a poor diet produces adverse changes in brain chemistry, which can affect things like behaviour, concentration, attention, motivation and so on. All of these obviously will have an impact on mental performance, including the taking of IQ tests and in particular the more 'biological' kind of intelligence involved in non-verbal IQ.

At about the same time, a scientific report came from Germany which lent more support to the idea that poor nutrition may affect a whole range of mental states and abilities. In a very large, carefully controlled study, psychologists at the University of Göttingen studied over a thousand men in their twenties. Some were found to have 'a chronically insufficient vitamin supply', which was discovered by taking blood samples and measuring the amount of vitamins in their blood (testing blood is the most accurate way of determining if someone is malnourished or not).

The men then took vitamin and mineral pills for a couple of months.

The German psychologists were surprised to find that many of the men felt a lot better – not just physically but mentally too. They were more self-confident and outgoing, and much more able to concentrate.

But again, the psychologists discovered exactly what I had in my prison experiments – the vitamins only 'worked' for those who were malnourished in the first place. The men whose nutrition had been OK before the experiment didn't improve at all.

The year 1990 has turned out to be very productive for the whole field. David Benton at Swansea University has done a number of further studies, each throwing more light on the topic. One was rather similar to the German study, in that he looked at the effect of supplementation on people's mood. But unlike the Germans, he didn't test vitamins, but just one of the minerals – the trace element called selenium.

For any real nutritional buff in Britain, selenium is of particular interest. Why in Britain? Because the UK is one of the few places in the world where, for perfectly non-sinister reasons, the soil is unusually low in selenium. Therefore, by and large, every Briton is selenium deficient (although if you ask our old friends the British government they won't agree – same old story, no RDA = no problem . . . no problem = no RDA). So David knew, without having to do any elaborate biochemical tests, that the forty adults he picked for his study were bound to be low in selenium.

What he got them to do was take a tablet every day for five weeks and then say how they felt; stop for six months; then take another tablet for five weeks and say how they felt again. Little did the people know, but only one set of tablets contained selenium (100 micrograms), the other was a cleverly disguised fake. What David discovered was that when people were on the real selenium pill they said they felt more composed and confident, less hostile and depressed, and generally more energetic and clearheaded. The effect of the selenium was so marked that the experiment is what statisticians call 'highly significant' – there is only a one in a thousand chance of it being a coincidence that people felt better on the selenium tablet.

So does this mean the selenium is the magic ingredient that's responsible for all the improvements we've been observing in IQ and behaviour?- Absolutely not. Many of the beneficial changes have occurred in experiments where selenium wasn't involved at all. The German psychologists, for example, used only vitamins, and yet they found exactly the same kind of positive mood changes as David Benton did with selenium.

I am quite sure that the explanation is that each one of the micronutrients – every vitamin and every mineral – has its part to play in helping us to be optimally healthy, happy, good-natured and bright . . . but more of that later.

As I write, David Benton is currently back again testing the full spectrum of vitamin and mineral supplements on children's IQ and attention span – this time with six year olds. Progress so far suggest that he's getting good results, further confirming the basic finding.

The year 1990 also saw the publication of a very intriguing article by Dr Richard Lynn, a psychologist at the University of Ulster. He's something of an expert on global trends in intelligence, and for the last ten years has been publishing international and historical comparisons of IQ. The reason I want to bring him into this book is that, from a completely different perspective, he has come to the same conclusion as David Benton and myself – that nutrition is a major factor in intelligence, and that this has been totally underestimated until now.

What has led him to this conclusion? He has found that from about the 1930s onwards there has been a consistent trend in the developed world, showing a rise in average IQ throughout the whole population. Why does Dr Lynn think it's explained by nutrition? He says the major reasons are as follows:

1. Over the past fifty years, average heights have increased at the same rate as IQ. Height is known to be related to nutrition.

2. Only non-verbal IQ has increased; for example in Britain non-verbal IQ has risen steadily every ten years by

about two and a half points, whereas verbal IQ has gone up by only half a point. (Remember, a rise only in non-verbal IQ was precisely what David Benton and I found in our earlier experiments.)

Dr Lynn has also unearthed a number of studies on diet and IQ from as far back as the 1940s, which proved further evidence to back our findings in the eighties.

In 1942 in New York, for example, a certain Dr Kugelmass reported on fourteen years' experience of giving 'nutritional therapy' (i.e. vitamin pills) to malnourished children between the ages of two and nine. Some of the children were classified as mentally retarded. Partly as a check on his therapy, he tested their IQ before and after treatment, and recorded some remarkable improvements. The forty-one retarded children showed an average IQ gain of ten points, and the fifty normal children he had treated had a gain of eighteen points. He found the gains most marked in the younger children under four. But once again, he found that if the children had not been malnourished to begin with, there was no increase in IQ.

Meanwhile psychologist Ruth Harrell had just started a three-year-long experiment tracking the growth of intelligence of over a hundred orphans between the ages of nine and nineteen in a children's home in Virginia. Every day between May 1941 and September 1944 she gave half the orphans supplements containing 2 milligrams of thiamine and the other half identical-looking placebo tablets. At various stages during their development, she measured a large range of intelligence-related abilities – tests of memory, arithmetic, reading, reaction time and so on – and she found that the children on extra thiamine had consistently better scores on every one of the tests.

We have seen in this chapter how the furore created by the 1988 *QED* programme resulted in an acceleration of further research to re-test the original findings of Dr Benton and myself. Not all of the studies have supported us; but where they have not, I am fairly certain that the reason is because the children were not really malnourished in the first place. Time and again in my own studies over the last ten years, that critical finding has shown up – if you're OK nutritionally in the first place, there'll be little chance of any improvement in behaviour or IQ. Experiments in this field are therefore only worth doing if you can be certain of the nutritional status of the children you're studying – and the only way to be sure of that is to do blood tests of every single child you test. The problem is that it takes time and money – lots of it. And over the past ten years I've had the time but not a lot of the money, so it has been a struggle to do the definitive experiment . . . until now.

Again the 1988 *QED* programme was the catalyst. It happened that one of the 10 million viewers of the programme was a remarkable man by the name of Graham Aaronson. Twenty years ago he set up a family trust to support important initiatives that might benefit society. He was so enthused by what he saw on *QED* that he decided on the spot to put the full resources of his charitable foundation behind a study that would establish once and for all whether or not nutritional supplements do really improve children's IQ.

The next chapter tells the full story of the experiment that he sponsored. It is the biggest and best experiment that has ever been done, and I predict that its conclusions will reverberate throughout the world of nutrition for decades to come.

References

Lancet 6 Aug. 1988, 335.
Lancet 24 Sept. 1988.
Lancet 31 March 1990, 744–747.
Lancet 12 May 1990, 1158–60.
'Selenium supplementation improves mood in a double-blind crossover trial' Benton, D., Cook, R. *Psychopharmacology*, 1991.

Lynn, R., 'The role of nutrition in secular increases in intelligence', *Person. individ. Diff.*, Vol. 11, 1990, No. 3., 273–285.

Kugelmass, I. et al., 'Nutritional improvement of child mentality', *Am. J. Med. Sci.* 1944, 208, 631–633.

Harrell, R., 'Mental responses to added thiamine', *Journal of Nutrition*, 1945, 31, 283–298.

Naismith D. et al, *Lancet* 6 Aug 1988 p. 335.

Benton D., Rippere V., *Lancet* 24 Sept 1988.

Crombie I. K. et al, *Lancet* 31 March 1990 pp. 744–747.

Benton D., Buts J-P., *Lancet* 12 May 1990 pp. 1158–60.

Heseker H. et al., Ernahrungs-Umschau 37 (1990) Heft 3 pp. 87–94.

7 The Dietary Research Foundation Experiment

Thus it was that in January 1989 the Dietary Research Foundation was born, under the chairmanship of Graham Aaronson, to investigate scientifically the links between diet, intelligence and behaviour.

Graham Aaronson QC is a man with two lives – he divides his time between living in Britain, where he is a top financial lawyer, and Israel, where he is financial adviser to the Israeli government. In addition to these two jobs, he and his wife Linda own a family trust devoted to charitable projects with particular emphasis on the welfare of adolescents. The Aaronsons were, for example, early pioneers of new rehabilitation schemes for ex-prisoners.

Graham had been impressed by the 1988 *QED* programme and what he saw as its extraordinary implications for society. If it was true that even in affluent Britain some children were malnourished because they ate a junk-food kind of diet, as the programme suggested, and that this affected their mental states, what impact might an improvment in their nutrition have on whole areas of social concern like education and crime? The question was too important to be ignored, Graham thought, too important not to be investigated thoroughly and without delay.

However, when a year had passed after the *QED* programme, and there had been no major response from any government or scientific authorities in Britain, Graham decided that the time had come to take the matter into his own hands.

So it was that a private individual, with no scientific background whatever, set out to organise a scientific experiment that would definitively answer a question that is arguably one of the most important issues in nutrition this century. In order for it to be definitive, Graham knew the experiment was going to have to be carried out both impeccably, and on a large scale. That meant it was going to be very expensive. And yet nothing daunted, he was prepared to back the study to the tune of over half a million pounds, the money donated by his own family charitable trust.

And yet there was no certainty that it would be successful – particularly as the previous studies on diet and intelligence had either failed, or been rubbished by most of the experts.

Despite his lack of a scientific background, Graham had remarkably good instincts about the way research in a controversial field should be conducted. His first act was to assemble a high-powered team of advisers. He felt he needed top experts in nutrition, psychology and statistics – and he got them! First to be recruited were two of the world's leading nutritionists, John Yudkin and Linus Pauling.

Dr John Yudkin, Emeritus Professor of Nutrition, was the creator of Europe's first university department of nutrition at London University in 1953. The author of some 300 scientific pieces of nutritional research, he, you may remember, had been one of the most vociferous 'establishment' critics of the origional *QED* programme and what it reported. Nevertheless, he was sufficiently open-minded to agree to help the Dietary Research Foundation conduct a large-scale experiment, and run the risk of being proved wrong!

Dr Linus Pauling, Emeritus Professor of Chemistry at Stanford University in California, is a Nobel Prize Laureate and is famous (some would say infamous) as a nutritionist for his invention of Orthomolecular Psychiatry – the theory that many mental illnesses can be cured by very large doses of vitamins. Professor Pauling is also the father of the idea that Vitamin C will cure the common cold. His views on nutrition are unorthodox and diametrically opposed to John Yudkin's; so it was useful to have both of them on the DRF's advisory panel to ensure a balanced approach.

Dr Hans Eysenck, Emeritus Professor of Psychology at London University's Institute of Psychiatry, is Britain's leading psychologist, and internatinally renowned for his groundbreaking research on a wide range of subjects. He also has a reputation for open-mindedness that has sometimes not endeared him to his fellow psychologists. His areas of expertise include personality, criminology and intelligence, and he was therefore another ideal adviser for the DRF project.

Also recruited was Dr Eric Peritz, Professor of Biostatistics at the Hebrew University, Jerusalem – one of Europe's leading statisticians, with enormous experience of the complexities of large-scale medical research.

Those four comprised the Dietary Research Foundation's Scientific Directorate.

Initially it was decided to do five experiments in five different countries – USA, Canada, Israel, Britain and Holland. Israeli paediatrician Dr Dov Tamir was appointed to mastermind the European end of things, and the American side was to be headed by myself. However, it soon became apparent that five experiments was over-ambitious, so the Directorate agreed on two: one in Britain, the other in the USA.

Organising the Trial

In July 1989 Graham Aaronson, Dr Tamir and I had a meeting with the Scientific Directorate to plan the research. The issue to be investigated was straightforward: does giving vitamin and mineral supplements to children increase their IQ? Simple question, but it took two days of concentrated discussion to work out how best to answer it.

First, what strength of supplement should the children be given? Professor Yudkin, who believed that children were probably by and large well nourished, argued that a pill containing half the Recommended Daily Amount of all the vitamins and minerals would surely be enough to bring every child up to proper nutritional health, since they would be getting most of the RDA in their food anyway.

I wasn't so sure, and suggested that the supplement should be stronger. I agreed with John Yudkin that a fifty per cent formula might bring the children up to the RDA levels, but who was to say the RDAs were correct? (Remember that historically the whole reason for the RDAs was to prevent only *physical* signs of malnutrition, not mental). I pointed out to the Directorate that, in calculating the RDAs, no one had ever considered IQ. So we might find that the proper vitamin and mineral levels for maximum mental performance were higher than the standard RDA.

After hours of debate we came to the following conclusion: we would do two separate experiments in Britain and California, involving four schools each. Because there was uncertainty about the ideal dose of vitamins and minerals, the children would be given three different strengths of supplement: containing either fifty per cent of the RDA, a hundred per cent RDA, or two hundred per cent RDA. My point had clearly been taken!

It was obvious to everyone that the experiment was going to be more complex than anything that had been done before. We were going to have to test four groups of childen – each group taking one of the three different supplement formulas, and one group receiving a fake placebo tablet containing nothing at all. Dr Peritz, the statistician, calculated that we would need to test a minimum of 400 children in the UK and the US to be sure of getting a reliable result that could not be explained away as coincidence.

Measuring IQ

There are two basic ways of measuring IQ – the quick way, and the slow way. The quick way is the one most people are familiar with. You get given a book of questions, and fill in the answers; there's normally a time limit of about twenty minutes. These were the kinds of tests David Benton and Gwilym Roberts used in their Welsh experiment shown on *QED*. They have the advantage of being cheap and easy to administer, particularly in a classroom setting, but they suffer from a major disadvantage – they are not always very accurate.

However the DRF study was going to be the largest and most definitive experiment ever done on nutrition and intelligence, and we recognised that our IQ tests had to be more sophisticated, in order to be as accurate and unchallengeable as possible. So, in addition to giving a standard 'classroom' IQ test, we decided to give each child a special individual assessment of IQ. To do this we would need to recruit a small army of psychologists trained to administer a sophisticated ten-part IQ test called the Wechsler Intelligence Scale for Children. The WISC test is a mini-marathon: it takes nearly an hour to complete, and involves intense concentration and cooperation between child and psychologist. It is therefore very expensive. Nevertheless it is the Rolls Royce of tests, and it would give us precise measurements of every child's IQ – so we had to have it.

As if that wasn't enough, the Scientific Directorate said they wanted two tests of reaction time, and one of personality. Following the methods I had used in US prisons, they also asked for blood-sample analyses of the children, in order to assess their exact levels of nutrition.

Having designed the experiment, we now had to carry it out. First hurdle, find the children.

In California we had little problem. I simply went along to some of my local schools, explained the importance of the project, showed them a copy of the 1988 *QED* programme, and quickly got the cooperation of four schools. But in Britain, things weren't so straightforward: many education authorities were reluctant to help, and it wasn't until the last minute that four schools in Barrow-in-Furness agreed to take part.

Thus, we had lined up two experiments each involving some 600 children aged between twelve and sixteen on either side of the Atlantic. The experiments began at about the same time in January 1990.

Taking the Tablets

The experiment was in three basic parts: stage one, test the children's IQ; stage two, give them the pills; stage three, test their IQ again to see if there had been any improvement.

In California, stage one was a mammoth task, involving 400 man-hours of WISC testing, 100 hours of blood sampling, and about the same again for the rest of the tests. It was over a month's work for more than twenty people.

That completed, it was time to give the children the vitamin and mineral supplements. We randomly divided our 600 children into four groups – three to take the three different strengths of real supplements, one to take identical-looking fake placebo tablets. Of course, nobody involved in the experiment knew who was taking which – it was the classic double-blind placebo-controlled trial. The pills were issued every day by the form teachers for a period of thirteen weeks; if for any reason the children missed their daily dose, the overseers made sure they got double rations the next day.

Meanwhile we prepared ourselves for stage three – equally mammoth, of course, as stage one. Because it was going to be such a lengthy job, we decided to start the testing procedure after ten weeks of pill-taking. We completed the whole lot in three weeks.

As you can imagine, we ended up with an absolute mass of data, which took us another month to compile. We then sent it to Professor Eric Peritz in Israel; as the statistician, he held the secret codes identifying which children had been receiving which of the four different pills. He was also the person who would work out if we had a significant result.

The Results

On 13 July 1990, everyone involved with the Dietary Research Foundation project convened in Great Britain to hear from Eric whether the experiment had worked.

As the cliché goes, you could have heard a pin drop when the professor stood up to announce his findings. 'My preliminary analysis of the experiment', he said in the dry manner most statisticians seem to adopt, 'is that we have got a definitive result. First major finding: there was no significant change in verbal IQ. Second major finding: there was no significant change in non-verbal IQ except in one group of children taking the vitamin and mineral pills. The change was a gain of approximately four IQ points.'

So it had worked! And in precisely the same way that both I and Dr David Benton had previously found in the smaller studies we reported in the 1988 *QED* programme – an increase in non-verbal IQ, none in verbal IQ.

I was pretty confident all along, of course, that our much larger-scale experiment for the DRF would be successful, but the Scientific Directorate had been less sure. Professor Eysenck, although favourably inclined to the idea that nutrition can affect IQ, nevertheless had originally given the experiment only a one in three chance of working. And as for Professor Yudkin, he had thought the idea so unlikely that he gave it odds of one in twenty! 'This is going to cause an international furore among nutritionists,' he said ruefully after Professor Peritz's announcement.

However, when Professor Peritz presented the results in more detail, Professor Yudkin got another shock.

It turned out that the supplement containing a hundred per cent of the RDA was the one that produced the biggest improvement in non-verbal IQ. Now remember, all these

Results of Dietary Research Foundation Trial on 600 US schoolchildren

Experimental group receiving:	Increase in IQ		True gain in IQ	
	Verbal	Non-verbal	Verbal	Non-verbal
0% RDA placebo	2.96	8.96	0.96	0.06
50% RDA supplement	0.54	10.06	−1.46	1.16
100% RDA supplement	2.83	12.57	0.83	3.67
200% RDA supplement	1.87	10.48	−0.13	1.58

NOTES

1. The 'true' gain in IQ takes into account the increase in IQ that normally occurs when a maturing child takes the same IQ test for the second time. During the three-month duration of the trial, gains of 2 verbal IQ points and 8.9 non-verbal IQ points were to be expected.

2. Certain children did not complete the course of tablets. If you exclude the children who had 50 or more tablets left in their bottles at the end of the experiment, the 'true gain' in non-verbal IQ rises to 4.42.

3. For the benefit of statisticians, the True Non-Verbal Gain of 4.42 is $p = .002$.

children were eating a normal kind of diet, which would be expected to provide, at the absolute minimum, fifty per cent of the RDA. So Professor Yudkin's original prediction that the fifty per cent RDA supplement on top of a normal diet would result in adequate nutrition in theory makes sense. But it was clearly not borne out by the results. The data seems to show that the human mind functions better on a normal diet *plus* a hundred per cent of the RDA – which implies that the RDA standards of vitamins and minerals set by government are too low.

British readers of this book should also be aware that the RDA levels we used in the DRF supplements were American, not British. You will recall I showed on pages 78 and 80 that the British RDAs are often much lower than the US ones. I shall deal with the serious implications of our findings for the UK RDAs in the next chapter.

But there's another interesting thing to be noticed from our DRF results. Look again at the two hundred per cent RDA figures. You'll see that the children on the two hundred per cent supplement, who might have been expected to make the biggest IQ gains because they were taking the strongest formula, actually didn't do very much better than the children on the fifty per cent pill. Why on earth not?

The reason is because more doesn't necessarily mean better, particularly when it comes to the minerals. In fact more can sometimes mean worse.

This was not the first time I had seen this happening. Back in 1987, when doing detailed blood-chemistry analyses of my academic high flyers, I found that greater levels of certain minerals tended to counteract the benefits of other nutrients – they seemed to interfere with the body's absorption processes. In the DRF study, this pattern was clearly being repeated. Later in the book, I'll return to this topic again, as it has important implications.

The four-point increase in non-verbal IQ we found in the DRF experiment is what scientists call 'statistically significant' – a jargon expression which means that it is highly unlikely that the findings can be explained away as mere coincidence. The 'p = .002' note I added to the results on page 115 for statisticians indicates that you would have to do our DRF experiment 500 times before you would come up with the same results by coincidence. For statisticians therefore, our results were highly significant.

But what about the real world? What good is a mere four-point increase in IQ, you may ask?

First, it's true that no one's going to join Mensa on four

extra IQ points, or become Albert Einstein, but it is still a substantial amount. Let me explain. If for example your child has an IQ of 100, that means that he ranks roughly half way up the intelligence scale in the population; i.e. fifty per cent of children will be more intelligent than him, and fifty per cent of children less intelligent. But if you increase his IQ to 104, he will rise twelve percentage points on the comparison scale; so now he becomes less intelligent than only thirty-eight per cent of other children, and more intelligent than sixty-two per cent of them. Quite a leg up in the IQ league. As statistician Eric Peritz put it: 'On the basis of the results of this experiment, if I had school-age children I would certainly think it sensible to give them vitamin and mineral pills in order to help them attain their full mental abilities.'

Secondly, bear in mind that the four-point gain applies to the whole group of 150 children who received the hundred per cent RDA formula. It is an average figure, and averages can hide an awful lot of variation. In fact when we looked at the data in detail, we found that three quarters of the children did not increase their IQ at all. But for the remaining twenty-seven per cent, there were really dramatic gains in IQ – from seven right up to twenty-five.

What's exciting about this finding is that it's following the same pattern that I found in my prison experiments: there, better nutrition improved behaviour, but not for everybody. Only about a third of the prisoners ever responded, and they always turned out to be the ones who were originally most malnourished.

So I suspect that the twenty-seven per cent of the schoolchildren whose IQ rose the most were also the most malnourished to begin with. At the time of writing (September 1990), however, I cannot be sure, as we are still in the process of collecting the blood-chemistry data.

There was another very dramatic effect of the study, and it had immediate practical benefits for the schoolteachers as well as the children.

Twice a year, all schoolchildren in the US are required by law to undergo a formal test of fourteen academic skills, including the 3Rs of reading, writing and arithmetic. This Comprehensive Test of Basic Skills is taken very seriously, not only by the pupils but the staff as well. The teachers' increases in pay, and sometimes their very jobs, depend on how well their pupils perform.

As it happens, our experimental period fell neatly between two CTBS examinations in autumn 1989 and spring 1990, so we were very interested to see whether the supplements would have any effect on the children's basic skills. When the results came out (see fig 10), I was gratified to find that there was a really dramatic difference.

The CTBS measures pupil's performance against a monthly universal standard. As the tests are done six months apart, children are expected to improve by the equivalent of at least half an academic year. We found that, as anticipated, the children who had taken the fake placebo tablets showed a gain of approximately six months. But the children receiving the hundred per cent RDA supplement did a lot better, showing gains of up to an entire academic year.

The British Study

Meanwhile, the results of the experiment in Barrow-in-Furness had also been analysed. Because of the difficulty in finding enough local psychologists trained to administer the WISC test, only about 100 children had been fully IQ tested. There was concern that the numbers would be too small to provide a statistically significant result. But the fear was unfounded.

The British children showed a similar response to the supplements as the children in the US, with an average gain of nearly four non-verbal IQ points. But, unlike in the US where we had found the hundred per cent formula worked the best, in Barrow it was the two hundred per cent RDA tablets that produced the most significant gains in IQ.

This finding was at first a puzzle until the daily records of the experiment were examined. It turned out that the Barrow children had been somewhat less assiduous in taking their daily supplements, and on average had only consumed half the required number of pills. Thus the fact that they had been actually receiving half the daily dose was a clear explanation of why the two hundred per cent RDA formula appeared to work the best.

As I write, the more detailed results of the DRF study have still to be analysed. As an aside, I might add that

fig 10

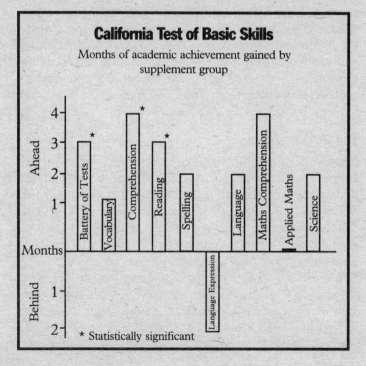

California Test of Basic Skills

Months of academic achievement gained by supplement group

unfortunately the British experiment did not provide enough data to be independently significant. But the US study alone is definitive enough for there now to be little doubt that good nutrition – either in the form of supplements or a healthy diet – improves both IQ and academic performance.

The enormous implications of these findings I shall explore in the next chapter.

8 The Implications

A few months ago, I received a letter from a young girl in Chicago, which really amused me. 'Dear Dr Schoenthaler', it said, 'I am writing to tell you that I have been taking the vitamin supplement you recommended, and it has really been very helpful. I started taking the pills two weeks ago, and I have noticed a very big improvement in my marks in maths. I have gone from the bottom to the top of my class. Could you please recommend a brand of supplement that will get me higher grades in English and History.'

Clearly there is no pill in the world that will teach a child that the Pilgrims left England and landed at Plymouth Rock in 1620. No amount of good nutrition will teach a child how to punctuate, appreciate poetry, or spell Thanksgiving. Knowledge comes from exposure to learning, either through experience, reading or formal teaching, and nothing else.

What our research suggests, however, is that good nutrition will make a child more receptive to any learning experience. Our studies have shown that well-nourished children are more able to concentrate on the task in hand, to pay attention, to reason and to remember.

So, in my view, the evidence is that good nutrition, while not making anyone smarter as such, will signficantly improve their potential to learn.

Let me give you a simple analogy. If you try and record a piece of music on a bad quality tape, it will be a poor recording; it will lack a lot of the original musical information. But a good tape will be able to 'absorb' more of the musical information, and reproduce more of the original sound. Giving children good nutrition is like putting a better tape on the tape-recorder. Their brains are more receptive to information, and so better able to absorb it.

This type of mental ability is sometimes called 'fluid intelligence'.

Fluid and Crystallised Intelligence

As I mentioned in Chapter 5, psychologists recognise that there are basically two types of intelligence. 'Crystallised' intelligence is the type that is learned and stored in one's memory; the older we get the more it improves, as new knowledge-bearing experiences are assimilated. For example, people who do well on difficult quizshows like *Mastermind* have very developed crystallised intelligence.

Fluid intelligence, on the other hand, cannot easily be learned because it involves the basic reasoning processes in the brain. People with highly developed fluid intelligence are likely to be descibed as quick-witted, sharp, or on-the-ball. It's the kind of intelligence we are to a large extent born with, and few psychologists would have thought it was able to be significantly improved in anyone – until now.

We now know that fluid intelligence *can* be improved by good nutrition. The experiments of Dr Benton and myself have shown a consistent effect of nutrition on non-verbal IQ – and non-verbal IQ tests are a measure specifically of fluid intelligence.

This is another reason why our new findings are likely to be such a bombshell: psychologists simply will not be able to believe that nutrition could possibly have such an effect. Of course, they recognise that *severe* malnutrition can affect intelligence. Hundreds of studies on deprived children in the Third World show that people who suffer from a physical deficiency disease through malnutrition also have impaired intelligence. But the impairment affects both types of intelligence – fluid and crystallised.

Whereas our studies have shown that marginal levels of malnutrition – even a small deficiency in a single vitamin or mineral – impairs only fluid intelligence.

This very specific finding gives us a clue about what may be happening in the brain to explain what is going on.

The Malnourished Brain

As I explained in Chapter 1, the brain is basically powered by oxygen and glucose arriving in the bloodstream – oxygen, of course, taken from the air and glucose from food.

In the case of the severely malnourished person, it is easy to understand that sheer lack of food will mean that little glucose actually gets to the brain. The whole functioning of the brain would start to break down – including of course intelligence.

But in the case of someone who is getting enough food, and therefore enough glucose, how could his intelligence be impaired? My theory, and it is only a theory at the moment, is based on the fact that vitamins and minerals are needed to convert glucose into the electrical energy that runs the brain. Six B vitamins and four minerals are involved in the process which converts oxygen into energy to power the brain – the so-called Aerobic Metabolism or the Krebs Cycle (see fig 11). The vitamins are thiamin (B1), riboflavin (B2), niacin (B3), pantothenic acid (B5), pyridoxine (B6), and biotin. The minerals are iron (Fe), magnesium (Mg), manganese (Mn), and phosphorous (P). If a deficiency existed in any of these ten nutrients, metabolism and brain function would be impaired.

However, these are not the only nutrients that impact brain function. Other vitamins and minerals are indirectly involved in absorption and transportation of the ten nutrients. For example, vitamin C increases the absorption

fig 11

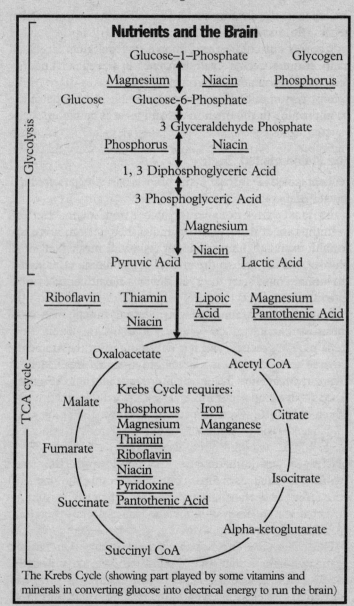

Nutrients and the Brain

Glycolysis

Glucose–1–Phosphate   Glycogen

Magnesium   Niacin   Phosphorus

Glucose   Glucose-6-Phosphate

3 Glyceraldehyde Phosphate

Phosphorus   Niacin

1, 3 Diphosphoglyceric Acid

3 Phosphoglyceric Acid

Magnesium

Niacin

Pyruvic Acid   Lactic Acid

TCA cycle

Riboflavin   Thiamin   Lipoic   Magnesium
Acid
Niacin   Pantothenic Acid

Oxaloacetate   Acetyl CoA

Krebs Cycle requires:

Malate   Phosphorus   Iron   Citrate
Magnesium   Manganese
Thiamin
Fumarate   Riboflavin
Niacin
Pyridoxine
Succinate   Pantothenic Acid   Isocitrate

Alpha-ketoglutarate

Succinyl CoA

The Krebs Cycle (showing part played by some vitamins and
minerals in converting glucose into electrical energy to run the brain)

of other essential nutrients like iron. The B vitamins folacin (folic acid) and B12 (cobalamin) are necessary for the making of the RNA and DNA and thus, new cells. New red blood cells are required every eight weeks to transport the other essential nutrients to where metabolism takes place in the brain. Chromium, as well as other minerals, regulates the permeability of cell membranes and is essential for releasing energy from glucose. The eight minerals calcium (Ca), magnesium (Mg), iron (Fe), copper (Cu), zinc (Zn), molybdenum (Mo), chromium (Cr), and selenium (Se) are parts of enzymes or activate enzymatic reactions that are essential for metabolism.

In fact, the bottom line is that twelve of the thirteen vitamins and ten minerals play either a direct or indirect role in the digestion, absorption, transportation, and eventual conversion of glucose into energy in the brain. Deficiencies in humans have been observed in all of them except phosphorus. It seems logical therefore that a lack of even one of the twenty-one nutrients could affect the full functioning of the brain.

Which is precisely what we have found in our studies: a lack of just one nutrient is all it takes to impair intelligence or worsen behaviour. The question raised by the DRF study, though, is when is a lack a lack?

The Ideal Nutrient Intake

When we were discussing the strengths of supplement to test in the DRF trial, each of us made a prediction about which of the three formulas would improve IQ the most.

Professor Yudkin was totally sceptical that the experiment would work at all, and so thought that none of the formulas would have any effect. But in the unlikely event of the experiment being positive, he said that the fifty per cent RDA formula would be more than enough to bring the children's nutritional levels to the hundred per cent level, and that the higher doses wouldn't produce any improvement at all, as they would be providing nutrients that were surplus to the body's requirements.

Professor Pauling felt the complete opposite. As one of the leading exponents of so-called megavitamin therapy, he believes that high doses of vitamins can sometimes have very beneficial effects on someone's health and feeling of well-being. And high doses for him does not mean just a little bit over the RDA, but sometimes two hundred times the RDA! So he naturally favoured our highest RDA formula – the one containing twice the RDA.

I disagreed with both of them, and said so.

On the basis of my previous research, I was sure that John Yudkin was too optimistic about what the minimum nutritional levels really are for the proper functioning of the human body, particularly as far as mental performance is concerned. But then John is a traditional nutritionist, representing the vast majority of expert opinion, so it was hardly likely that he would believe otherwise.

I felt John Yudkin was wrong because my studies of academic high flyers revealed that they had much more than the hundred per cent RDA levels of vitamins and minerals in their blood. I was certain therefore that 'supernutrition' above the levels recommended by nutritionists really was extremely beneficial.

On the other hand, I had also discovered that too high a level of nutrients could sometimes paradoxically have a negative effect. Obviously, very high doses of some vitamins and minerals can be toxic (see Appendix for vitamins, p. 197), but that wasn't what I was talking about. I had found that relatively modest levels of nutrients – particularly some of the minerals – sometimes can produce a sort of interference effect. It's all to do with the proper balance. For example, if a mineral like calcium is present in too high a concentration, it can interfere with the way iron is absorbed, and thus negate its positive effects. When you get into supernutrition territory, the right ratios are just as important as the actual levels of vitamins and minerals themselves.

So, when I looked at the two hundred per cent formula in detail, I could see that some of the nutrients were out of balance with each other, and were in danger of causing unwelcome interference effects.

That's why I was able correctly to predict that the hundred per cent RDA supplement, although not the strongest formula, would nevertheless have the biggest effect.

What does it Mean?

The DRF experiment raises two major practical questions: 1. What are the ideal levels of vitamins and minerals? and 2. Can we receive those levels from our food alone, without resorting to supplements? Let's take the second point first.

Why are nutritionists so very confident that the levels of vitamins and minerals they recommend are correct? Part of the answer is that the RDAs are the levels most people actually receive from their food. The nutritionists' reasoning goes something like this: our population gets from the food they eat an average of so many micrograms of this or that vitamin and mineral. People seem to be reasonably healthy, so it follows that the levels of nutrients they are getting in their food must be enough. Those levels therefore will be the basis of our RDAs.

There's also a second reason why nutritionists think that what people actually eat should be enough for them.

When you press nutritionists hard, you will find most of them have a touching faith in the power of Evolution. They argue that Evolution would not have arranged things so that human beings could not get adequate nourishment from the natural products of the earth – fruits, crops, and animals. If the available food was not sufficiently nourishing, they argue, the processes of natural selection would have ensured that people became adapted to the nutritional environment they found themselves in, and so evolved into beings that could be wholly nourished from the food around them.

Superficially this is an attractive, commonsense idea. But if you look at it more closely, it turns out to be too simplistic.

It implies first of all that Evolution is a perfect process which somehow omnipotently and omnisciently arranges things so that every being becomes perfectly adapted to his environment, and therefore perfectly evolved. This is the kind of evolutionary fundamentalism propounded by many popular natural history gurus, but, in my view, it is simply not appropriate to human development.

First, if humans were so perfectly wrought nutritionally, why did the Evolutionary Creator organise things so that we are not able to manufacture our own vitamin C, and instead are wholly dependent on finding it in food? Surely it would have been more advantageous to be able to synthesise it from other constituents of our food as we do with some of the other vitamins?

Secondly, Evolution is a very slow process; it can therefore take little account of the fact that we are living in a very rapidly changing world, in which our lifestyles are altering very fast – including our nutrition.

In the developed world, the last fifty years has seen a revolution in our food supply. With the growth of population and urbanisation, we have had the rise of food 'manufacture'. It starts on the farm, with massive use of fertilisers. Fertilisers have, it is true, increased yields, but at the expense of some of the nutrients – many of the vitamins and minerals become depleted in the presence of high levels of fertiliser chemicals. Also, before food reaches us, it is often subjected to factory-style processing – canning, boiling, freezing, refining – which further reduces the natural content of vitamins and minerals, leading to a loss of more vital nutrients.

So, even supposing the Creator had made a perfect world in which our food supply could provide us with all the nutrients we need, Man has certainly rendered it imperfect.

Thirdly, there are all the environmental changes of the twentieth century, and in particular pollution. The by-products of modern industry, farming and transportation produce toxic compounds some of which actively reduce the amount of vitamins and minerals in our body. They are called anti-nutrients. The lead found in leaded petrol, for example, is an anti-nutrient, as it interferes with the action of the very beneficial mineral zinc.

Fourthly, the stress of modern living itself makes many more demands on our bodily systems than ever before. And even nutritionists will admit that an organism under stress has a much increased need for vitamins and minerals.

Fifthly, there are some parts of the world where food simply cannot contain all the necessary nutrients because of local climatic or geological conditions. In Britain, for example, it is impossible for people to get enough selenium in their diet, as there is not enough of it in the soil.

Finally, the results of the DRF experiment showed that the supplement formula that had the most beneficial effect on mental performance was the one containing a hundred per cent of the United States RDA. Since the children must have been already getting at least fifty per cent of the RDA from their food, it follows that people will have impaired mental performance below the one hundred and fifty per cent RDA level. Can everyone get that amount from their food alone? It seems to me unlikely.

The inevitable conclusion, therefore, is that taking a vitamin and mineral supplement is indeed necessary if we are to be sure of being properly nourished. But that must be only *as a supplement* to good eating.

My advice on how best to do this is the subject of the chapter after next. Before that I want to alert you to another very important aspect of children's nutrition, namely, the years before school age and in particular the critical months after and indeed *before* they are born.

9 Mother and Baby

As we have seen, the official view is that there is no real malnutrition in Britain today. Expert nutritionists and government documents promote the view that virtually everyone gets enough vitamins and minerals from the average British diet, and that any public concern about the quality of our children's food is because the public does not understand nutrition.

But in the last twenty years, the experts have begun to concede that there might be a number of exceptions; they admit that there are a few so-called 'risk groups' for whom the otherwise splendid British diet may not be good enough – the very old, the very young, pregnant and breast-feeding mothers, and alcoholics. In this chapter, we'll look at the latest research data on mothers, babies and infants, and reveal startling new evidence that here again relatively low levels of malnutrition may affect the brains of infants – even before they are born.

It's been known for over fifty years just how critical a mother's nutrition can be to the well-being of the growing child inside her. In a large-scale study in the 1940s of mothers-to-be, doctors in Canada discovered for the first time that even a slighly depleted diet can cause serious complications both for mum and her developing child. In fact, they found that a bad diet may sometimes actually kill. This astonishing discovery was made very simply; 400 pregnant women with a poor diet were randomly either given instruction and help in improving their nutrient intake, or left alone to eat their normal diet. They were then monitored throughout pregnancy, labour, and the first six months after giving birth. The comparisons were striking: while pregnant, the poor diet mothers had many more complications – for example, more vaginal bleeding, more severe vomiting, more pre-eclampsia. They also had more complications during labour.

But what really shocked the researchers was the effects on the infants; the poorly nourished mothers had more than twice the number of premature babies, and six times the number of miscarriages and stillbirths. Of course, the vast majority of the babies did survive, but here too the doctors found the differences persisted: the babies of mothers with a poor diet had more illnesses like colds and even pneumonia. The researchers also noted: 'The difference in the appearance of the infants in the good diet group was strikingly better than those born of mothers on a poor pre-natal diet', and they concluded: 'Nutrition . . . is the first step and a most important one, in assuring sound structural development during the period of rapid foetal growth, and in producing a healthy infant during its first months of life. The application of the principles of nutrition could not be more important in any other period of life than during pregnancy.'

Not long after the Canadian discovery, the British government introduced a scheme by which doctors could prescribe vitamin and mineral supplements to pregnant mothers they felt to be particularly at risk. And yet many of the nutrition-related problems in pregnancy first identified by the Canadian researchers in 1942 are still around in Britain today. In fact Britain has some of the highest rates of infant deaths in Europe, and some of the lowest birth weights. Spina bifida in particular has a particularly tragic record. Britain's 7000 cases a year are again among the highest in Europe, and Northern Ireland's rate of 3.4 spina bifida cases per thousand, literally the highest for any nation in the world.

Like stillbirth and premature babies, spina bifida too now seems to be related to malnutrition.

It was Professor Richard Smithells of Leeds University, an expert in paediatrics and child health, who first discovered the link between spina bifida and lack of vitamins – in fact one in particular, the B vitamin called folic acid. Folic acid is found in dark green vegetables such as broccoli, green cabbage and spinach, and in liver and kidneys. Most pregnant women are at risk of not having enough of it, as the developing foetus takes an awful lot for itself. Two studies by Smithells in the late 1970s and early eighties, and another by Professor Michael Laurence in Cardiff, showed convincing evidence that giving vitamin supplements containing folic acid considerably reduce the incidence of spina bifida for high-risk mothers.

But, as ever, the experts pooh-poohed the evidence. Indeed, as journalist Geoffrey Cannon revealed in his book, *The Politics of Food*, officialdom deliberately turned its back on the problem. Cannon found that in 1979 an official DHSS handbook listed the RDA of folic acid as 300 micrograms for adults, and 500 micrograms for pregnant women; but that when the same report was reprinted in 1981, the RDA for folic acid had been withdrawn. The explanation for this official sleight of hand? It came in 1982 from the Medical Research Council: 'It should be noted that the normal daily requirement for folic acid for normal adults, and more particularly for the developing embryo, is not known.' What a strange statement to make. After all, three years earlier the authorities clearly thought they did have enough knowledge to set an RDA figure for pregnant women. So why was the RDA withdrawn? Perhaps the real reason was the shocking finding in a 1979 survey of the Great British Diet, which showed widespread folic acid deficiency, especially in pregnant women who were found on average to be consuming less than half of the new RDA. The thought may have been: 'There's a problem with folic acid deficiency according to our RDAs. So let's drop the RDA – and *abracadabra* the problem's gone away!' As ever, the official line is: *There is no malnutrition in Britain*, and so any evidence of malnutrition must be ignored or suppressed.

The spina bifida story is important because it showed for the first time there may be a link between marginal levels of malnutrition in pregnancy and problems with the development of the baby's central nervous system. And that could have obvious consequences for much less dramatic impairments – like poor intelligence and bad behaviour.

Derek Bryce-Smith is another scientist who has been concerned about children's nutrition in the womb. As Professor of Chemistry at Reading University, Bryce-Smith provided most of the evidence for the hazards of lead, which resulted in the recent change-over to lead-free petrol in Britain. In 1990 he and a number of colleagues published the results of a study on eighty new-born babies in the Merseyside area of Britain. Actually what they studied was the nutrient content of the mothers' placenta when it had been expelled after birth. Using some very sophisticated techniques, they measured twenty-six different trace elements in the tissue, a number of them the minerals found in nutritional supplements. They found striking connections between the levels of some of the minerals, and the newborn baby's weight and the size of its head.

Iron, chromium, copper, calcium, zinc and cobalt were all higher in the mothers who had the biggest babies, and correspondingly lower in the mothers of the small babies. Smaller babies were also born to mothers with higher quantities of lead in their placenta. Now low birthweight is not that rare in Britain – in fact one in fifteen newborns are below the generally agreed acceptable minimum weight of 2½ kilos (5 lbs 8 ozs). So the findings are very important to the 46 000 mums in Britain a year who bear underweight babies – and to their doctors. Bryce-Smith and his colleagues put it bluntly: 'We have identified a number of important nutrient factors that, other than iron and sometimes calcium, are at present ignored in antenatal care.' Quite so. And ignored, they might have added, by government and its DHSS: a. who have no RDAs for chromium, copper, zinc or cobalt; and b. whose free nutritional supplement for low-income pregnant mothers contains not a single mineral.

So what are the implications of the Bryce-Smith research for the subject of this book? The variation in the head sizes of the babies, and its connection with the mother's nutritional status, is the crucial finding. For according to the paediatric text-books, head size is an important measure of the baby's brain development, which in turn is associated with intelligence.

A recent study in Scotland, for example, followed up children who had low weight at birth (below 2½ kg). At the age of ten their IQ was found to be an average of four and a half IQ points lower than similar children who had had a more normal birthweight. Sceptical nutritionists might retort: 'That may have nothing to do with nutrition. It would be due to a variety of social factors that are very difficult to control for.' Well, there have also been many studies on cases of identical twins where one twin was born smaller than the other (doctors think the difference in size is caused by one twin getting a reduced blood supply from the placenta, thereby reducing its supply of nutrients in the womb). Despite the fact that the twins had identical upbringings, when they were IQ-tested, *up to thirteen years later*, the twins who had been born bigger had an average IQ *five points higher* than their twin brother or sister.

How can nutrition as a foetus possibly affect intelligence thirteen years later? We now know that, in the womb, it's the brain of the foetus that develops most rapidly, and in fact most of the ten billion neurones it will have as an adult will have grown by five months after conception. Professor Bryce-Smith says the infant brain is very vulnerable: 'Neuronal development can certainly be disturbed by . . . general maternal malnutrition before birth . . . and more specifically by pre-natal zinc deficiency, with irreversible effects on the behaviour of the offspring.'

Zinc is in fact widely deficient among the British population – in fact, lack of zinc is a problem in many developed countries. Why? According to Bryce-Smith, it's partly to do with modern farming methods: artificial phosphate fertilisers interfere with the way food crops naturally take up zinc from the soil, and intensive farming in general depletes the organic matter from the soil, which has a similar effect on zinc uptake.

So just how much at risk from zinc deficiency are pregnant mothers in Britain? According to the British government's own figures, the answer is badly. A Ministry of Agriculture survey in 1981 showed that a Briton's *average* daily intake of zinc was 10 mg. Again, it's the pregnant mother who is most affected, because the typical British diet provides less than the daily amount (15 mg) recommended for her by the United States government. (As with folic acid, because there is a widespread zinc deficiency in Britain, Britain does not have an RDA for zinc. Getting the picture?)

Professor Bryce-Smith is worried by his new findings: 'Chemical influences on brain development and function tend to operate most strongly on the young and the foetus. Changed brain chemistry can alter . . . behaviour, cognition [and] social interactions. The relevant chemical factors include neurotoxic pollutants in general (especially lead), and certain common nutrient deficiencies, particularly of zinc. Zinc is seriously deficient in many UK diets.'

Derek Bryce-Smith, despite the fact that he's an eminent professor of chemistry and was the man who first alerted the authorities to the hazards of lead in petrol, tends to be regarded as a bit of a crank by the medical and scientific establishment. So it's unlikely that his warnings about malnutrition in pregnancy will be taken any notice of by the so-called experts.

But they might listen to Dr Alan Lucas.

Dr Lucas is a nutritional scientist at the prestigious Dunn Nutrition Laboratory in Cambridge. His boss is Dr Roger Whitehead, whom we have already met in Chapter 4; he, you may remember, was one of the nutritionists most hostile to the 1988 *QED* programme 'Your Child's Diet on Trial', and the results of the Welsh school study reported in *The Lancet*. He, in common with the rest of the scientific and medical establishment, questions the whole idea of extra vitamins and minerals having any effects on the brain in a well-nourished country like Britain. So it would be unlikely that any member of his staff would come up with research findings that contradicted him. But Dr Alan Lucas has done just that.

On 23 June 1990 in *The Lancet*, Dr Lucas, together with eight scientific colleagues, reported the results of a study of the mental development of over 400 premature babies.

During roughly the first four weeks of life, the doctors had fed the babies one of two kinds of milk-formula feeds. On a random basis each baby had been given either a standard baby formula, containing normal levels of vitamins and minerals, or a special formula with extra vitamins and minerals.

The first thing the doctors found was that the babies on the supplemented formula put on weight faster, and had quicker head-size growth. But it was when they looked at the babies eighteen months later that they found the most startling differences. The babies were put through a battery of tests to assess their so-called 'motor' skills (sense of balance etc), their 'social maturity', and their mental development. To their astonishment the doctors found very significant differences. The babies on the supplemented diet were ahead on every one of the tests – for example, they had a fourteen-point advantage on motor skills, and a nine-point advantage in mental development, particularly language. The effect was especially marked in boys, and in the babies who had originally been the smallest.

The doctors were staggered: 'It is surprising,' they wrote, 'that the very short period of dietary manipulation in our study had such prolonged consequences.' Remember, the babies had been fed the special supplemented formula for only the first *month* or so of life. And yet as much as a year and a half later, there were clear long-term effects on their mental development. The doctors wondered what might have caused it: The special formula contained nearly 40% more protein and 18% more energy than the standard formula. Differences between the formulas in micronutrient and mineral content were even greater. Although emphasis has (traditionally) been given to the importance of meeting protein requirements in premature babies to achieve maximum growth, possibly the intake of some other nutrient or nutrients might be of fundamental as yet unrecognised importance. These data . . . provide objective evidence . . . that early nutrition may affect later neurodevelopment in man.

So there we have it. Evidence from one of the bastions of the nutritional establishment that supplementing diets with vitamins and minerals may affect mental development. I predict that Dr Lucas's findings, together with those from Professor Bryce-Smith, are going to cause as much of a revolution in ante- and post-natal nutrition as the data from Dr Benton and myself on intelligence and behaviour in older children.

But astonishingly, a lot of this was known some time ago. Way back in 1955 doctors wanted to see what effect good nutrition of mothers in pregnancy would have on the intelligence of their babies. So they gave vitamin supplements to over 600 mothers during pregnancy; however, as soon as the babies were born the supplements were stopped. Neither the mothers nor the children received any further extra nutrition. Years later, when the IQ of the children was measured at the ages of three and four, and compared to the children of similar mothers who had not taken supplements, the children's IQ was an average of six and a half IQ points higher.

Ten years ago, another study in America again showed the effect of good nutrition in pregnancy on the subsequent IQ of the children. The researchers gave nutritional supplements to mothers in the last three months of pregnancy, and also during the first year of the baby's life. They then compared those babies to their nearest brother or sister who had not been given the early extra nutrition. The results were astonishing: when tested between five and seven years later, the children who had been the 'supplemented babies' had higher IQs, attention-span, visual-motor coordination, and higher marks in school. They also were better behaved.

Findings like these give yet more support to the work of Dr Benton and myself, but they have been largely ignored. And yet these studies have been published in respectable scientific journals, and have therefore been available for any nutritionist or scientist to refer to. But no, nutritionists still continue to assert that there cannot possibly be any connection between diet and IQ.

So let's leave the so-called experts wallowing in their ignorance, and see what practical steps parents should take in the light of this new research.

Practical Steps for Parents

One thing is abundantly clear: the vitamin supplements given free by the DHSS to low-income mothers are totally inadequate. Likewise the free vitamin drops for the under fives. These supplements contain only Vitamins A, C, and D. It may of course turn out in further research that these three vitamins are the only ones pregnant mothers and newborns need. But I doubt it. So I would advise that infants and mothers-to-be take a full-spectrum supplement as outlined in Chapter 10, if there's any hint of a nutritional deficiency. It's particularly important as well that the supplement has the correct zinc/iron ratio, as too much iron can interfere with the baby's uptake of zinc (see Chapter 10 for the kinds of supplements I recommend).

But remember, as I keep on saying in this book, vitamin and mineral supplements are just that – *supplements*. Mothers-to-be should continue to eat as good a diet as they can afford (see p. 186 for some diet suggestions), and they should of course breast-feed their babies unless there are medical reasons not to.

That should take care of mother and baby from conception to three months old. What then?

It may sound a bit early, but I would recommend trying to start baby on solids at about three months. Some dieticians might disagree with me, but the evidence does seem to point towards three to six months being the time at which mother's breast milk is declining, and the baby is putting on a lot of weight and growing rapidly.

There's another reason too. The latest research also suggests that three to six months is the time at which a baby develops the food preferences it will continue to have for the rest of its life. Whatever tastes and textures the infant is exposed to in that three-month time-frame will determine what it will enjoy eating right through childhood and even adulthood. By twelve months old, it's too late; the research data shows that it's very difficult to get a baby to accept new tastes after its first birthday. But up to six months, it will learn to accept whatever it is given – even things it initially doesn't appear to like. This astonishing discovery was recently made by a team of American doctors who fed a whole range of strange tastes to babies. They found that, no matter how initially unpleasant the taste, they needed to offer a baby an unpleasant food a maximum of fourteen times, and hey presto! baby would automatically like it. But only in that three to six months window; any later and no matter how hard they tried, how much they cajoled, baby wouldn't have any of it.

'Nature is really neat and pretty,' says Birmingham University psychologist Dr Gillian Harris. She has also been looking at infant feeding and agrees that three to six months is the best time to introduce solids.

Imagine what it must have been like for man's early ancestors, with children being born into a primitive natural environment with a variety of wild foods available, some wholesome, others poisonous. It makes an awful lot of sense for the baby to be able to learn to accept anything its mother gives it while it's still in the nursing stage; whatever the food tastes like, if mother gives it to the child, it's bound to be nutritious. But as soon as the child is a year old and able to move around by itself, the situation's reversed. At that age there's a lot of sense in the child *rejecting* any new taste he comes across – that interesting wild berry he's never tasted before could be poisonous.

The implications for our own times are crystal clear. If you want your baby to have a good diet when he/she grows up, you must introduce him/her to the right foods before six months.

So what kinds of foods should baby be fed? The manufacturers won't want to hear this, but baby foods are not the answer. Those little cans of puréed meats, vegetables and fruit, although handy, cannot possibly have the nutrient value of fresh food prepared at home. For a start, do you imagine all baby-food manufacturers always use the best cuts of meat or the freshest vegetables, when all they're going to do is grind them up into a bland mess? Secondly, the canning process itself, with the enormously high temperatures necessary to sterilise the contents, reduces vitamins considerably. Tacitly, they admit this. Look at the labels of some of the leading brands in Britain. 'Apples with Vitamin C', Heinz proudly exclaim – as if a real apple doesn't contain any vitamin C and nice Mr Heinz has generously improved on nature. What it really means, of course, is that Mr Heinz's processing has removed quite a lot of the vitamin C from the apple that nature had put in. They're all at it: Cow & Gate – 'Apple & Pear: Pure juice for babies, with Vitamin C'.

Quite simply, the best diet for a baby is what nature intended – whatever is enjoyed by the rest of the family. There are very few food items which adults eat that cannot be freshly prepared for baby in a minced, puréed or diced form – providing, of course, that what the family eats is itself half-way decent nutritionally. Unfortunately, as we have seen in Chapter 5, many families in Britain either don't know what the proper foods are, or more likely cannot afford them. For them, a nutritional supplement for baby (as well as themselves) is a must. Again, you'll find my recommendations in Chapter 10.

References

Ebbs, J.H. et al., *Canadian Medical Association Journal*, Jan 1942, Vol. 46, No. 1.

Smithells R.W. et al., *Lancet* 16 Feb 1980, 1; 339–40.

Smithells R.W. et al., *Lancet* 19 Dec 1981, 2; 8240–61.

Illsley, R., and Mitchell, R.G., *Low birthweight: a medical psychological and social study*, Chichester: Wiley. Cited in Lynn, R., op. cit.

Bruce-Smith D. et al., J. Nutr. Med 1990, 1; 19–26.

Bruce-Smith D., Chem. Soc. Rev. 1985, 15; 93–123.

Lucas A. et al., *Lancet* 1990, 335; 1477–81.

Six studies 1965 to 1986, cited in Lynn, R. op. cit.

'Environmental chemical influences on behaviour and mentation', *Chem. Soc. Rev*, 1986, 15, 93–123.

Lyon, T.D.B. et. al., *MAFF Food Surveillance Paper, No. 5*, 1981 HMSO/ *Br. J. Nutr.* 1979, 42, 413.

Harrel, Ruth F., et. al., 'The influence of vitamin supplementation of the diets of Pregnant and Lactating Women on the Intelligence of their Offspring', *Metabolism*, 1956, Vol. 5, 555–562.

Hicks, L.E., et. al., *Am. J. Public Health*, 1982; 72; 1110–1118.

Whitehead R.G., Am. J. Clin. Nutr. 1985, 41; 447–458

Harris G. and Booth D.A., J. Rep. Inf. Psych. 1987, 5; 97–104.

10 Choosing a Rewarding Diet and Supplements

First of all, remember: a good supplement is not an adequate replacement for a good diet. A good supplement is an insurance policy to cover any areas in which your diet is deficient. However, a supplement should never be deemed a replacement for attempting to eat well. So what steps should you take to maximise the nutritional value of your diet?

Making sound suggestions on nutrition would be an easy task if I knew who you were. Many of you will be 'meat eaters' like the typical American; some of you will not be eating red meat; others will be 'vegetarian', some of whom will be avoiding all animal products. Thus, it makes sense to start with very basic principles upon which all nutritionists seem to agree, something they call ABCV. This stands for Adequacy, Balance, Calorie control (or nutrient density) and Variety.

A Balanced Diet

Back in 1980, the National Academy of Sciences Food and Nutrition Board reviewed the way typical Americans ate, and the type of diet that was ideal. They broke foods down into four groups: complex carbohydrates, protein, fats, and simple carbohydrates (sugar and alcohol). Interestingly, there is almost no difference between British and Americans in the ratios they consume of these four types of food. (The differences never exceed one per cent in any category.)

Fig 12 illustrates what the average Briton's and Americans

diet consists of as regards fat, sugar, complex carbohydrate and protein. This is juxtaposed with what the Board recommended: an ideal diet balanced with no more than thirty per cent fat, ten per cent sugar, at least forty-eight per cent complex carbohydrate, and twelve per cent protein. These figures are amongst the most important in this book.

fig 12

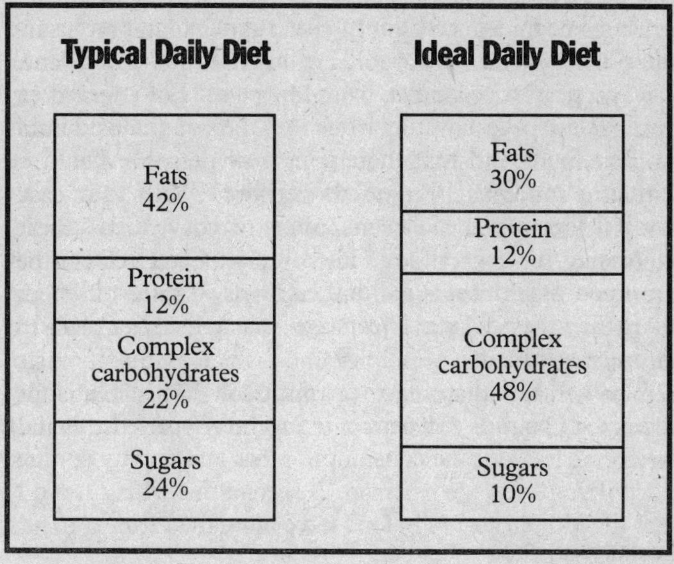

Typical Daily Diet	Ideal Daily Diet
Fats 42%	Fats 30%
Protein 12%	Protein 12%
Complex carbohydrates 22%	Complex carbohydrates 48%
Sugars 24%	Sugars 10%

Both the Americans and the British eat about the right amount of protein on average, twelve per cent. The typical American's diet is likely to contain more red meats, while the English eat more cheese and cold cuts, but they both average out to about twelve per cent protein.

However, the primary problem that both nations have with a balanced diet is in the area of excessive fats and sugars, with a deficiency of complex carbohydrates. Fat consumption needs to be cut by about a third and sugar consumption by half, and these lost calories should be replaced by complex carbohydrates.

The main sources of complex carbohydrates are cereals (such as wheat, rice, oats, corn and rye) and cereal products (such as bread, pasta and chappatis), starchy vegetables (such as potatoes, parsnips, yams and sweet potatoes) and pulses (beans, lentils and peas).

The greatest source of fats and sugar, for most Americans and Britons, is highly processed foods – 'junk food'.

Many people would doubt that twenty-four per cent of their diet is sugar, and would be surprised to learn that the average person consumes over 140 pounds of sugar every year. These people would argue that they seldom add sugar to their foods and that there is no way that they could be eating as much as 140 pounds per year. What they don't know is that over the years manufacturers have been steadily increasing the sugars they hide in foods. Fig 13 shows that most people add less sugar to their foods, but are still eating more than they did some years ago, due to the sugars hidden in processed foods.

You will see that sugar consumption has increased by twenty-six pounds per person in just sixty years. In the last twenty years, average consumption has gone up by another thirty-five pounds per person. A second disturbing trend is that the hidden sugars in food have more than tripled in just sixty years.

Since 1970 things have got worse. When you buy a take-away hamburger, you would be surprised by how much the 1990 version differs from the 1970 one. For one thing, every hamburger bun is loaded with sugar. The ketchup used to be primarily tomato and vinegar: today it is primarily tomato and sugar. Even the onions and pickles are soaked in sugar. The manufacturers do this because they have learned that a sweet hamburger sells better. The good news is that people have become more and more sophisticated about

fig 13

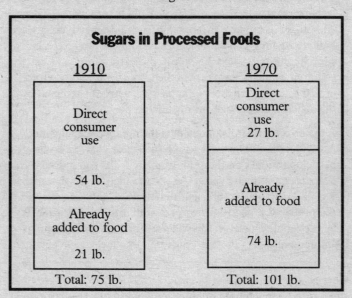

sugars and add less and less each year to their food. However, the manufacturers have offset the improvements in food selection by hiding sugars in the processed foods you buy.

At the end of the day, the only way to achieve a balanced and healthy diet, is to use more fresh fruit, vegetables, and whole-grain products, and cut down on highly processed foods that are likely to contain a lot of sugar or fat.

An Adequate Diet

If you want to eat an adequate diet, you must pay attention to two questions. First, what are your staple foods, i.e., your primary source of carbohydrate calories? Second, are they

The Green movement has been gaining momentum over the last few years with an increasing demand for organic produce. Although it is unlikely that organic fruit and vegetables have a higher vitamin content than conventional produce, their superior flavour could be worth the extra effort and cost. Children who may have turned their nose up at watery lettuce or bland-tasting tomatoes or apples will surely be tempted by the delicious flavours of the organic versions.

A major concern at the moment is the number and amount of pesticides used. There are strong suspicions that the levels of pesticide residues on the skins of many fruits and indeed the outer leaves of many vegetables are too high. Even thorough washing may not be sufficient to remove them completely so it's probably a good idea to peel your fruit and vegetables before eating. However, this will result in some loss of vitamins and minerals.

the tissue from a whole plant or a dismembered (partitioned) part of the plant?

For example, people of Asian descent typically have rice as their staple food. Historically, Asians ate brown or whole-grain rice, but during the last century white rice replaced brown rice. People who eat a great deal of white rice are likely to be deficient in iron and B vitamins, if they do not make a conscious effort to get those nutrients elsewhere.

Traditional West Indian diets have sweet potatoes, yams, eddoes and plantain as their staple carbohydrates. These foods contain surprisingly high amounts of vitamin A, vitamin B6, folic acid, vitamin C and vitamin E as well as dietary fibre and so make an important contribution to the overall diet. However, prolonged boiling and overcooking can lead to substantial losses of many of these valuable vitamins as they can leach out into the cooking water. Incidentally, look out for the orange-fleshed varieties of sweet potato as these contain more vitamin A than the pale varieties. West Indian diets also include lots of vitamin and mineral-laden fruits – mangoes, paw paw, pineapple, oranges, melon and soursop – as well as many vegetables. All excellent ingredients in a healthy diet.

If your ancestors were strictly British, your typical staple carbohydrate has been the potato. Although not sufficient alone, combined with another vegetable, such as cabbage, the two will provide adequate quantities of all vitamins and minerals. However, it is vital that these vegetables are properly prepared. The main source of minerals and vitamins in a simple potato is in the slightly green area immediately below the skin. Once a potato is peeled and that area is lost, most of the nutrients (though not the calories) are lost. So the nutritional content of chips is very poor, but a jacket potato is excellent. A boiled potato boiled in its skin is half way between. If the liquid in which it is boiled is saved and consumed, many of the nutrients that have leached out during cooking will be saved too. On the other hand, if the potato is peeled before boiling, it is little better than the chips, which have almost no nutritional value.

Cabbage is also very nutritious, although less popular today than potato. This is most nutritious when served raw in a salad. If it is boiled and the liquid is consumed as a broth or soup, it is also very nutritious. However, just as with the potato the process of boiling causes most of the nutrients to be leached into the water.

The same criticisms can be levelled at white bread as can be levelled at white rice. Most of the vitamins and minerals have been discarded with the loss of the bran and the germ. A wholegrain bread made of wheat has substantial quantities of twenty-two essential nutrients. Its cousin, white bread, contains just as many calories, but only four nutrients.

Your main source of carbohydrate should not be chips, crisps, white rice, or white bread. None of these foods is very nutritious. Restrict them to occasional treats, rather than use them as part of your daily diet.

Many parents wonder how they can get a child to eat potatoes in any form other than fat-laden chips and crisps. Suggest serving jacket potatoes topped with cheese and a little meat or vegetable. Cheese with broccoli, cheese with bacon bits, sour cream with chives or onions make a nutritious meal that children will enjoy. If they do not like their potato done one way, then try another. Although I hardly recommend it, I do know one child who loves jacket potato with tomato ketchup and onion. The point is – let your child invent a topping the way he or she likes, to go with the jacket potato.

The same can be said of wholegrain bread. If your child or you do not like the taste or grainy texture of one brand, switch and try another. Don't assume that all whole grains taste the same, nor that all manufacturers make even the same grain taste similarly. I found that my wife did not like the first five loaves of different brands of wholewheat bread I purchased for us. The sixth brand she not only likes, but prefers to white bread. The point is that one should not be limited to only wheat breads or only one bakery. There are nine different very nutritious grains. Experiment and explore. You will find a few that you prefer to white bread if you try. Finally, don't cut out white bread completely. There are some sandwiches that just do not taste right without white bread, and if you feel like having it, go ahead. But just remember that white breads are not very nutritious and should be used sparingly rather than every day.

In terms of adequacy, you must ask yourself: what proportion of your diet comes from whole foods, as opposed to 'partitioned' foods? By partitioned foods, we mean milled grains (wheat and rice); purified sugars, fats, and oils; and alcohol. Nearly two thirds of the typical British diet comes from these partitioned foods, which, ideally, should not make up more than one third of your daily calorie intake. Calories can be deceptive. A beautiful fresh salad may contain 200 or 300 calories. Putting three tablespoons of your favourite blue-cheese dressing on it will raise the calorie content to an unhealthy 900 calories. So think about using just one teaspoonful, or choosing a healthier salad dressing with less calories.

Ideally, you should make some changes to your diet every day. The idea behind variety is to increase the types of foods you eat so that if any typical food is not so nutritious as it should be, the deficiency is made up by other foods. To add variety, you might try one new food each week.

A Calorie-Controlled Diet

The last principle is calorie control or nutrient density. The aim here is get all the necessary nutrients combined with a limited number of calories. If your daily supply of calories is not accompanied by all the required nutrients two things can happen. You will end up not being properly fed for that day, or you will eat more to eliminate the deficit. By eating more you risk weight gain. The ideal solution is to choose foods that contain lots of nutrients per calorie. The alternatives are to exercise more, or gain weight, or be poorly nourished. Many of us, myself included, accept these basic truths, but find it difficult in our busy schedules to get the ideal amount of exercise that goes with a good diet. It is easy to become well nourished but overweight, due to a lack of proper exercise.

Nutritionists have reduced the above theories and principles to a very simple formula called the 'Four Food Group Plan' and the 'Modified Four Food Group Plan'. Following either of them will improve nutrition, since they contain the majority of the thirty-nine nutrients essential for life.

The Four Food Group Plan

recommends the following each day for a growing child in this case four years old. (The cup refers to an average size tea-cup.)

- Three cups, or four ¾ cup servings of milk or milk products
- One egg and two servings of other meat or meat substitutes
- Four or more servings of fruit and vegetables
- Four or more servings of breads and cereals.

Some more detailed recommendations about a sensible daily diet for children may be found on page 184.

The Case for Supplements

At least half the American population uses vitamin-mineral supplements regularly. Collectively, American consumers pay over 4 billion dollars a year for them. On the other hand, half the American population does not use them. You may ask: Which half of the population is right? And if we should take a supplement, how should we chose the right one?

A number of studies have been done in the West looking at the nutritional status of large sections of the population. These studies consistently found that in each country a substantial minority is not well nourished. Many would prefer to ignore this fact, that even in the most affluent nations in the world there are these numbers of malnourished people – mostly women and children.

Those in favour of taking supplements correctly point out that in the presence of such widespread deficiencies, taking a daily supplement to ensure that we do get the nutrients we need makes good sense. There is a lot of evidence to support this notion. First, western foods today are nothing like what our forefathers ate. Two thirds of our foods are highly processed (they consist of white breads, sugars, purified oils, and other dismembered tissues that have lost the majority of their nutritional value in processing). Secondly, many of our vegetables and fruits are picked before they are ripe and do not contain the quantity of nutrients that fruits ripened on the tree and vegetables ripened on the plant contain. Thirdly, many of the soils in which we grow our foods have been depleted of essential nutrients and generate produce that is low on selected minerals and vitamins. Fourthly, our forms of cooking, particularly boiling, causes much of the vitamins and minerals to be discarded in the liquids. Fifthly, it is known that stress and illness increase our nutrient needs severalfold, and that extra nutrition is warranted in today's high-stress societies. Sixthly, processing of foods often destroys selected nutrients. Seventhly, and most compelling of all, many people report that they simply feel better when they take supplements. It is difficult to argue with success.

The Case against Supplements

Still, there are those who take issue with the claim that people feel better on supplements. They argue that the improvement is psychological, a placebo effect. There is certainly some truth to this.

The primary argument against supplements is not so much against the idea in general as against high-dose supplements. The fear is that high doses may cause harm. The supporters of supplements tell us that these fears are largely unwarranted, but the public would have to be well educated on the signs and symptoms of vitamin-mineral toxicity in order to determine if this were true. Unfortunately, only a few people recognise the signs of short-term acute toxic doses. In the last ten years, I myself have seen two cases.

The Food and Drug Administration in the US has attempted to come to grips with this problem over the past few years. They have found that some minerals like selenium become toxic at only five times the recommended daily allowances. A few of the fat soluble vitamins (vitamin D in particular) can also become toxic at just 5 times the United States' RDA. For water-soluble vitamins, toxicity is almost unknown. Many people take quantities that exceed the US RDAs by several hundred per cent (with the exception of folic acid) and seem to suffer no ill effects.

What is important is that everyone should know that high doses of any mineral and any fat-soluble vitamin can lead to toxicity when consumed over a long period. It follows that taking high doses of minerals or fat-soluble vitamins should be done only under the direction of a physician. In contrast, the risk from water-soluble vitamins is minimal.

The Consensus

Those who debate the benefits and risks often conclude with examining whether selected populations should take a supplement. The critics concede that people with conditions shown in the the box opposite would benefit from taking a supplement.

One can see that the list of people who would potentially benefit from supplements is larger than that of those who do not need them. Let's look closely at the first group, 'people with low energy intakes'. How low is too low? In other words, if a person carefully followed the Four Food Group Plan and paid strict attention to every calorie he or she ate with regard to fats and sugars, how many calories would be needed? The answer, depending on the culture, is nearly 2000 calories per day! That's also the amount of food you must eat to get enough vitamins and minerals. However, for many people that's not possible; most of us don't have the time or appetite to eat anything like that quantity of food. For example, no woman consumes that much, and neither do two-thirds of men; and the average child only eats about a

---

People who will Benefit from Taking a Supplement

★ People with low energy intakes such as habitual slimmers
★ The elderly
★ People who eat monotonous diets
★ People who eat bizarre diets
★ People with any illness that curbs appetite
★ People taking medications which may interfere with the body's use of nutrients, such as seizure medication
★ People with illnesses which impair absorption of nutrients (these include diseases of the liver, gallbladder, pancreas, and digestive system)
★ People who have diseases, infections, or injuries
★ People who have undergone or about to undergo surgery
★ Women who are pregnant
★ Women who are lactating
★ Strict vegetarians
★ Women who bleed profusely during menstruation
★ People whose calcium intakes are too low

SOURCE: Hamilton Whitney and Sizer (1983)

---

thousand calories a day. So virtually everyone will benefit from a supplement.

Nevertheless, it's important to get your basic diet right initially, and then supplement that with a daily pill as an insurance policy. That's what a lot of the nutritional experts themselves do, although you won't find many of them admitting it. For example, a recent survey revealed that the majority of registered dieticians in the USA take a daily supplement – despite the fact that their official public stance is that it's not necessary.

So what supplement should you buy?

Selecting a Supplement

Following the previous release of my research on the first *QED* programme in 1988, a massive public demand for vitamin-mineral supplements literally cleared the shelves of most shops that sell such products. I had mixed emotions when I heard that this had happened. On the one hand, the taking of supplements will make many people brighter. On the other hand, many people undoubtedly wasted their money buying very poor products and a few people may have hurt themselves by ingesting massive amounts daily for a long period of time.

Some people will actually harm themselves taking supplements if they do not take them wisely. They erroneously believe that if a little helps a bit, a lot will help even more. This is analogous to finding that you can light a candle easily with a match. But using a blowtorch the next time does not accomplish the job any better and you are likely to be burned in the process. More than the necessary dose will not only not help, it can be dangerous.

Remember, when you shop, that your purpose is to find an inexpensive, nutritionally well-balanced, proper dose, and proper form supplement and nothing else. This means that you should not be swayed by promotions that certain products contain the mystery ingredient to give you more 'go', 'vitality', 'for those with active lives', or 'for a better sex life'. These are simply promotions designed to attract your attention.

Don't be impressed by pretty packaging or an interestingly shaped bottle. Look only at what is in the bottle and at the price.

There are a number of products to avoid. I would not give my family pills that were advertised as 'organic' or 'natural' unless they sold for the same price. The reason is that those terms do not have any legal meaning, and are not likely to offer anything more for my money. I tend to avoid products labelled 'high potency', since they often contain dose levels that are not balanced. I would never purchase a tonic preparation, as they are largely alcohol. Pills containing parsley, alfalfa, and other vegetables such as you could find in a salad are poor choices since making your own salad is always far cheaper. Compare prices.

Let's go over the major factors that should never be ignored. First, avoid any multi-vitamin that contains only three or four vitamins. These formulas often contain vitamins A, D, and E. They are among the worst supplements available in terms of protecting yourself against nutritional deficiencies. It is important to remember that there are thirteen vitamins that should be in a sound multi-vitamin supplement. The thirteen essential vitamins are: thiamin (B1), riboflavin (B2), niacin (B3), pantothenic acid (B5), pyridoxine (B6), folic acid or folacin, cobalamin (B12), biotin, vitamin A, vitamin D, vitamin E, vitamin C or ascorbic acid, and vitamin K.

So you see how a pill containing only three or four nutrients does not provide even minimal protection. A number of companies sell products that contain about ten vitamins. They usually leave out biotin, pantothenic acid, and/or vitamin K. I would never buy one of these brands. Insist on all thirteen in your supplements.

Many people make the mistake of buying only a multiple vitamin preparation and ignore the minerals. This is also a poor choice. People who have vitamin deficiencies are just as likely to have mineral deficiencies and both affect health and behaviour. The better supplements contain a minimum of ten specific minerals. The ten essential minerals are: calcium, iron, magnesium, zinc, copper, chromium, selenium, molybdenum, iodine, and manganese.

In short, a good supplement should not contain less than these thirteen vitamins and ten minerals. It does not matter whether the vitamins and minerals are packaged together in one pill or in two pills, although some manufacturers will try to promote separate pills as being better.

Now that you have eliminated any products that do not have at least twenty-three nutrients, you need to start looking at dose levels. You would think that the vitamin-mineral companies would automatically provide equal coverage of these essential vitamins and minerals, but they don't for two reasons. First, some of the nutrients, for example, biotin, are far more expensive than others. In fact biotin costs as much as the rest of the B-complex vitamins combined when it is placed into a pill. It is hardly surprising that only two or three British companies (out of the scores who sell supplements) bother to include more than ten per cent of the US RDA of biotin. Secondly, manufacturers use different dose strengths for the sake of being different, which they then promote as being better. The truth of the matter is that they are usually different purely for the sake of advertising.

To return to dose levels for our twenty-three nutrients, my recommendation is simple. I strongly recommend that each be provided at a hundred per cent of the United States' RDA with the exception of calcium and magnesium which can be as low as twenty per cent. I recommend a lower dose level of magnesium and calcium for one reason: it is impossible to get a hundred per cent of the US RDA into one reasonable-sized multi-vitamin-mineral pill. If you want a hundred per cent of the RDA of all twenty-three nutrients, you will have to buy the extra calcium and magnesium in two additional pills. This is not a bad idea, but I am trying to limit your initial selection to just one or two daily pills that are the most effective.

My choice of a hundred per cent of the US RDA as a dose level (with the exception of calcium and magnesium at twenty per cent) was not an arbitrary one. Of a total of five different-strength formulas, to date I have found that this formula is the best in terms of raising intelligence, with three other formulas being inferior. For example, I found that twice the number of children will produce large gains in non-verbal IQ when taking this formula as opposed to one which contains slightly less or even slightly more nutrients.

Since very few supplement brands in Britain state the per cent of the US RDAs on the side, you really need to have a copy of what they are when shopping. Bear in mind, too, that all forms of these nutrients are not equally absorbed into the system. Thus, I not only recommend paying attention to the dose level, but to the specific form of the nutrient. I recommend purchasing the nutrients, in the amounts, and using the ingredients as shown below.

Recommended Nutrients, Amounts and Ingredients

VITAMINS	*Amount*	*US RDA*	*Ingredients*
Vitamin A	5000 IU	100%	Vitamin A acetate
Folic acid	400 mcg	100%	Folic acid
Biotin	300 mcg	100%	Biotin
Vitamin C	60 mg	100%	Ascorbic acid
Vitamin D	400 IU	100%	Vitamin D3
Vitamin E	30 IU	100%	D-Alpha tocopherol
Thiamin (B1)	1.5 mg	100%	Thiamin mono-nitrate or thiamin HCL
Riboflavin (B2)	1.7 mg	100%	Riboflavin
Niacin (B3)	20 mg	100%	Nicotinamide or niacinamide
Pantothenic acid (B5)	10 mg	100%	Calcium pantothenate or d-calcium pantothenate
Pyridoxine (B6)	2 mg	100%	Pyridoxine HCL or pyridoxal 5-phosphate
Vitamin B12 (Cobalamin)	5 mcg	100%	Vitamin B12
Vitamin K (Phytonadione)	50 mcg	**	Vitamin K

Recommended Nutrients, Amounts and Ingredients

MINERALS	Amount	US RDA*	Ingredients
Calcium	200 mg	20%	Dicalcium phosphate or calcium carbonate
Magnesium	80 mg	20%	Magnesium oxide or magnesium carbonate
Iron	15 mg	100%	Ferrous funerate
Zinc	15 mg	100%	Zinc gluconate or zinc citrate
Iodine	150 mcg	100%	Potassium iodide
Copper	2 mg	100%	Copper gluconate
Manganese	3.5 mg	100%	Manganese sulphate or manganese gluconate
Chromium	125 mcg	100%	Chromium amino acid or chromium orotate
Selenium	70 mcg	100%	Selenomethionine
Molybdenum	150 mcg	100%	Sodium molybdate

* The US RDA was established for the labelling of packages to aid the consumer which differs from the 1989 RDA which is designed for 18 different categories of people. This table refers to the US RDAs.

The reader may wonder why I have included the form that each nutrient is presented as well as its dose strength. The reasoning is two-fold. First, the different forms have different rates of absorption into the body. The form in which calcium is presented, for example, will change the percentage of the calcium that is absorbed by as much as fifty per cent. Secondly, nutrients in a pill are not totally like nutrients in whole foods. Several compete for absorption.

For example, calcium hinders magnesium and iron absorption, and magnesium hinders iron and calcium absorption. Zinc hinders copper absorption, and copper lowers zinc absorption. Thus, a slight imbalance in copper of just one milligram can have a major adverse impact on zinc. Every form of the nutrients mentioned I have examined and confirmed that they result in the desired blood-nutrient concentrations. Thus, I highly recommend not only these nutrients, and dose levels, but the forms I have personally researched. For several nutrients I have suggested either of two forms. For example I have used both thiamin mononitrate and thiamin HCL. I am currently completing a study that will determine which of these forms I have used successfully is the best, but for the time being, I recommend the forms mentioned.

I wish I could state that brand x, y, and z are the perfect formulas which can be purchased at your corner store. Instead, I have examined the leading British products and been able to rank order three products that are readily available. My first choice is a product made by Healthcrafts called 'Vitachieve'. This is for eleven to seventeen year olds. (There is also a version called 'Junior Vitachieve' for seven to ten year olds.) This product not only contains all twenty-three nutrients I have tested, but it also has them at the dosages I used as well as the form I have studied. I suggest it is worth the extra effort to look for it. My second choice is Seven Seas 'Multivitamins and Minerals'. It contains almost the same nutrients, and the dose levels are fairly close, although the forms are not the same. If I could not find the Healthcrafts product, I would consider the Seven Seas product. My third choice would be a product called 'Tandem IQ'. The strengths of the formula are not so good as the Healthcrafts or Seven Seas products, but at least the formula contains nearly all the right nutrients. (This product is made specifically for children over the age of six.)

There is one exception to the above rules and that pertains to children with behavioural problems, such as hyperkinesis, insubordination, or even violence and antisocial behaviour. I found a slightly higher-dose formula worked well with them. It contains the same minerals, but three times the US RDA for most of the water-soluble vitamins (i.e., B1, B2, B3, B5, B6, and B12). For children who are sensitive to artificial food colours and flavours (such as those on the Feingold Programme), I highly recommend this formula. It is sold in Great Britain under the label 'Vital Life Multi-Vitamin' and 'Vital Life Multi-Mineral'. It has the advantage of being hypo-allergenic and is the product I used in my Oklahoma studies. It has the disadvantage of being far more expensive than the Healthcrafts product. Thus, with the exception of people who need a hypo-allergenic formula, my first recommendation would be to use the Healthcrafts product called 'Vitachieve', and my second recommendation (if that did not help) would be to try the more expensive Vital Life product. In the long run, one should use the formula that produces the most noticeable results. If the products produce equal results, I would use the cheaper Healthcrafts product.

Some people are willing to take more than a daily supplement and want more protection against deficiencies. The higher cost may or may not be warranted since we have not researched that area thoroughly. However, for those who want more protection, I would recommend 500 mg daily of vitamin C. My selection of this dose level is based on three factors. First, our ancestors consumed approximately this amount, and it is theoretically consistent with human evolution. Secondly, there is limited empirical evidence that the dose level has positive effects on health. Thirdly, there is not even one case of toxicity at this dose level. My second recommendation would be to take the US RDA of calcium which is about a 800 mg each day. The absorption of calcium is far superior when it comes with a little vitamin D and magnesium in the formula. Beyond these recommendations, taking more supplements is likely to offer little benefit.

11   Food for Thought

I have occasionally been introduced at speaking engagements as the world's leading criminologist specialising in nutrition, behaviour and intelligence. Although it may sound impressive, that title has been easy to earn as I am also the only academic criminologist who specialises in this field. It illustrates just how novel the whole field is, and how out-on-a-limb my work has been.

Perhaps therefore it may be thought arrogant of me to have written a popular book about my research, when it has received so little support from my fellow scientists.

I am under no illusions about what criticisms scientists may make of what they read. First they may point out that very little of my research has been published in any of the well-known journals of science.

There is a kind of unofficial yardstick of quality among scientists – the more respectable the journal any research is published in, the more respectable the research. But the trouble is that the converse is also true: if the research you are doing is not 'respectable', no respectable journal will touch it.

It's classic Catch-22.

The studies I have been doing over the last decade have been looking at questions most experts feel should not even be asked, let alone investigated. For example, the over-whelming majority of my fellow criminologists think it is simply not theoretically possible for criminal behaviour to be affected by nutrition, period. So any research producing data that questions that assumption must, by definition, be incorrect. The editorial policy of criminology journals is decided by a panel of criminologists who naturally will not want to publish anything that comes to incorrect conclusions. As a result, my research does not get published. Consequently, scientists at large conclude quite reasonably that, if it has not been published, it must be incorrect.

It's the same story with all the other branches of science my studies connect with. No psychology, educational or nutritional journal wants to know.

However, my research has of course been published; most of it has appeared in a journal that has the same high editorial standards as any other – except that very few scientists have ever heard of it! It's called the *International Journal of Biosocial Research* and it specialises in the effects of environmental factors on human performance. The field is a new and exciting one, but it's not yet respectable. Therefore neither is the journal, so very few read it.

The upshot is that most scientists never get to see my research data. If they do, they often get it second-hand, filtered through journalists of varying degrees of competence and understanding.

, The second criticism my scientific readers will make is that the conclusions I have come to in this book are unsubstantiated, or at the very least premature. They will point out that little of what I claim to have discovered has been 'independently replicated'.

Replication is another yardstick to evaluate research. Before accepting that any claim is well and truly proved, scientists insist that more than one person should have done an independent investigation, and come to the same conclusion. But in my case, I freely admit that independent replication has been patchy.

On the connection between nutrition and mental performance, there have admittedly been a number of studies, ranging from the work of Ruth Harrell in the early 1940s to

David Benton's in the late eighties, that do provide independent replication. But, on the other hand, two recent studies failed to find any connection. Sceptical scientists, therefore, can easily choose to accept the negative verdicts, and dismiss the positive findings as having been the result of sloppy research.

It's even easier to be sceptical about my work on behaviour. Although I have made 25 separate studies inside 20 institutions, all of which demonstrated that better nutrition improves behaviour, the plain fact is that no other scientist has found the same thing – because no one has ever bothered to investigate it.

According to the strict rules of science, therefore, I am not really justified in making any of the claims in this book.

On the other hand, if you're an unprejudiced reader, you will have judged my claims with an open mind, and I hope come to the conclusion that there really is something in the idea that good nutrition can improve mental performance – leading either to better behaviour or to a higher IQ. As you know, I started out very sceptically, and took a long time to be convinced. But after ten years' work, I am certain that the effect is real. But why can I be so certain?

First, there's a pattern to my results that is very striking: time and again, no matter which prisoners I studied, no matter how I improved their nutrition, I consistently found antisocial behaviour improving by about forty per cent across the board, with the maximum improvement in prisoners who were already malnourished.

The same pattern shows up too in many of the experiments on IQ, and these were sometimes done, remember, by scientists other than myself.

Secondly, the findings hang together theoretically: maximum improvement occurring in the most malnourished is precisely what you would expect to find if the basic theory is sound.

Third, the results can be explained biochemically:

although the data is not yet complete, there are strong preliminary indications that the nutrients which have most effect on behaviour and IQ are the very ones known to be specifically involved in brain function. And the fact that only non-verbal intelligence is affected also indicates a biological explanation.

It all seems to make logical sense, and therefore I feel totally justified in presenting my data to the general public in this book. It's too important for you not to know about it.

What should be Done?

Having broken one unwritten rule of science by making unequivocal claims about the validity of my findings, why not break another – by indulging in a little crystal-ball-gazing? Let's speculate about the effects these new discoveries might have if people really begin to believe them?

I have already discussed what I think individual people should do at a day-to-day level, but it's worth repeating. You should try to eat as good and varied a diet as you can afford, but if you suspect that for any reason, financial, medical, practical or whatever, that you're not getting the nutrients you need, take a good-quality vitamin and mineral supplement. Pregnant mothers in particular should keep their levels of nutrients up during the first critical months of pregnancy when their baby's brain is developing. Children should be encouraged to eat well, but again, if parents suspect they are not, give them a daily supplement.

Supplements, remember though, are just that – supplements; they are not a substitute for good eating. No matter how many supplements you take, poor eating habits will take their toll – too much fat, too little fibre, insufficient carbohydrate and protein will all make you feel worse physically, and so probably impair your mental performance as well. They'll also shorten your life, which is the ultimate in mental impairment!

In short, be well nourished, and you will be at your mental and physical best.

But what about society as a whole? What should 'the authorities' do with these new discoveries?

Law and Order

During the rough ride I had when investigating the effect of high-sugar diets on juvenile delinquents, a number of criticisms of my work came from those who were concerned that criminals would start to use my theories as an excuse for their criminality. My critics were concerned that offenders might claim that it was their bad diet that made them commit the crime, and so attempt to evade responsibility, and therefore punishment.

Their fear is not entirely unfounded. Diet and crime is an idea that has already found its way into the courts. In California one enterprising lawyer successfully had his client's sentence reduced by invoking what has popularly been branded 'The Twinkie Defence' ('Twinkie' is a particularly sugary confection, and, as such, archetypal 'junk'). The lawyer said his homicidal client was a junk-food addict, and claimed the bad diet was affecting his health, and that therefore a possible life sentence for murder should be commuted because of diminished responsibility.

In Britain, too, a juvenile delinquent was recently discharged for a relatively minor crime because the defence was able to prove that he was allergic to potatoes.

So does this mean that every criminal will now be able to use food as a defence?

Provided the courts treat the issue seriously, the answer is that a criminal will be able to use food as a mitigating factor, no more and no less than he can at present use drink, drugs, poor family relations, inadequate education, racism, peer group influence, poverty and unemployment.

In the future, if my conclusions become widely accepted,

defence lawyers may well feel it valuable to have their clients blood-tested for nutritional status, in order to see whether malnutrition might be a mitigating factor. However, the courts are unlikely to accept that at face value, and might require corroborating evidence about the accused's brain chemistry, and request a test of his brain waves (by the way, over half the convicted violent offenders in the USA have abnormal brain-wave patterns). If the test confirms malnutrition, the courts might well order a course of nutritional therapy.

As it happens, something like this is already taking place on a small scale in Britain. In Barrow-in-Furness, an organisation calling itself the South Cumbria Alternative Sentencing Option has been set up to help local magistrates courts deal with persistent juvenile offenders, in whom there has been a history of violent behaviour. SCASO analyses the children's eating habits, and if they see a serious nutritional deficiency, they report back to the courts, who may then recommend giving therapy in the form of diet counselling and vitamin and mineral supplements. So far only a handful of children have been treated in this way, but the results seem promising – not one of them has committed any more violent offences, and some are completely reformed characters.

If the idea were to be adopted nationally, it's difficult to estimate what effect it might have on levels of crime. No research has ever been done outside a prison environment. But I have no doubt that treating persistent offenders with supplements and diet counselling is bound to have some effect, albeit probably only on a minority.

This is a point that both my critics and supporters occasionally get wrong: I do not make the claim that a good diet will cure crime – there are a vast number of social, genetic, environmental and personal factors that turn people into criminals. What I am saying, however, is that there is a substantial minority of offenders for whom malnutrition may be one important element of their behaviour, and that correcting it may tip the balance towards adopting a more socially acceptable lifestyle.

We know that nearly seventy per cent of all serious crimes (murder, rape, assault, robbery, and burglary) are committed by only about seven per cent of the population. And this seven per cent does not respond to either punishment or rehabilitation. Now it may be that these people are not biologically normal, and that their brains are not 'wired' in the same way as everybody else. In the future, I can imagine nutrition being used to correct these abnormalities, and so enable the offender to be more easily rehabilitated.

What effect would a nutrition policy have on crime levels? To be honest, I cannot really predict. But assuming only a modest ten per cent reduction, there would be significant savings to society – in terms of police and courtroom time, and less pressure on our prisons. Remember, every single prisoner costs the British taxpayer over £250 a week! It would also make society at large marginally less violent, loutish and dangerous.

Of course, I can feel much more confident about the effects of a nutrition policy within prisons. On the basis of my research, I can predict that the average prison would find immediate benefits for internal discipline, with an almost guaranteed reduction in violence of at least thirty per cent, simply by giving each inmate a daily vitamin and mineral supplement – costing a mere 5 pence.

Enough said.

Education

It goes without saying that if non-verbal IQ, the measure of fluid intelligence, can be increased by better nutrition, academic standards would certainly rise if schoolchildren were encouraged to eat a better diet. In Britain the easiest way to do that would be re-introduce the mandatory school-meal system. However, these days, the idea of government intervening in the lives and decisions of its citizens is increasingly unfashionable – the 'nanny state' is out, personal responsibility is in. So it is unlikely in the present climate that good nutrition would ever be fostered officially in Britain's school system, whatever its benefits.

Nevertheless, one could imagine other ways in which nutritional standards might be made to rise within the population. First, there might be so many millions of readers of this book that the whole of Britain will get the message! Less fancifully, the food manufacturers might recognise that the nutritional health of their customers is partly their responsibility, and that it is no longer sufficient for them to be producing foods that look good, taste good, but actually don't do very much good. Instead of adding all their artificial colours and flavours, could they not put back all those nutrients their processing took out? They've already done it with breakfast cereals, albeit in a half-hearted way, so what's to stop them extending the idea to all processed and manufactured foods?

Whatever the means, if children's nutrition were to improve generally, by how much would academic standards rise? At our present state of knowledge, it is difficult to say. Our recent work in California suggests that academic gains which are the equivalent of six months' schooling can be achieved. This is not to say, however, that thousands of little Tommys will suddenly understand Euclidean geometry, for example, without ever having heard of it. What it does mean, however, is that they will be able to grasp geometrical concepts more easily, so enabling them to learn faster and more efficiently. These gains will apply across the board, and particularly in the non-verbal areas of learning – abstract thought, problem solving and visual-spatial tasks.

Teachers may ask, however, is it really intelligence that is being improved by good nutrition, or is it something else that affects intelligence?

As yet the research data are not complete enough for us to

be able to say. We know that non-verbal IQ is the element of intelligence that is most affected. But is it non-verbal intelligence itself that is improved, or is it the application of that intelligence? Some people maintain that, if there is an effect of nutrition on IQ, it is 'merely' that things like concentration and attention-span are improved, and not intelligence *per se*. However, this may be playing with words. Intelligence only becomes manifest when it actually does something. Thus, however intelligent you are, if you cannot concentrate on the task in hand, you cannot use your intelligence. The net result is the same as if you were not intelligent.

Whatever the reason, as our schools in California have found to their delight, better-nourished children will definitely do better in class.

The RDAs

Another implication of some of our very latest research is that the Recommended Daily Allowances would appear to need wholesale revision, particularly in Britain.

The Dietary Research Foundation study clearly showed that the supplement formula which improved mental functioning the best was the one set at a hundred per cent of the United States RDA for all the vitamins and minerals. Which in practical terms means that, because the children must already have been receiving at the very least a fair proportion of the US RDA from their normal food intake, the US RDAs themselves are too low.

If the US RDAs are too low, then the British RDAs must be seriously adrift. Remember that nutritional experts in the UK have set some of the UK RDAs at half the US values, and consider that most vitamins and minerals do not even need an RDA figure at all.

In the past the attitude of nutritionists, particularly in Britain, has been: if we see no physical deficiency disease, then there's no problem. I predict that that view will now have to change. Nutritionists will have to wake up to the fact that, when calculating RDAs, they must take account of healthy mental functioning as well as physical.

Malnutrition itself will need to be redefined. Since we now know that even marginal levels of malnutrition can diminish our human capacities, each vitamin and mineral will have to be tested for its effects on mental performance and psychological health. If, for example, as Dr Benton has found, a lack of selenium impairs people's sense of well-being, that impairment should be classified as a deficiency disease – just like scurvy was in the eighteenth century. Selenium will therefore have to be tested to find the dose level that produces maximum well-being, and an RDA deduced. The same tests will have to be done for every other nutrient, not just on mood, but also of course on behaviour, intelligence, and mental and psychological functioning in general.

The implications for the world of nutrition are truly revolutionary. First, at an immediate practical level, I suspect that some of the RDAs will be radically different from what they are today.

But secondly, and more fundamentally, it will entail a total shift in attitude – from the old philosophy that is content merely to prevent disease, to the new approach where the goal is to promote optimum human functioning. The yardstick for adequate nutrition must no longer be the mere absence of pathological symptoms, but the point at which the human organism is at peak performance.

Of course, it would be naïve to think that this nutrition revolution would solve all our social, educational and personal problems. Life is much too complex for that. But it would help each one of us to achieve a higher state of physical and mental health, and so enable us to use what capacities we have been born with to the full.

At the end of the day, that is surely what life is all about.

Appendices

Major Food Sources of Vitamins and Minerals

Vitamins

Vitamin A	Liver, oily fish, margarine, whole milk, meat, carrots, tomatoes, dark green vegetables
Thiamin	Bread (especially wholegrain), wholegrain cereals, fortified breakfast cereals, meat, pulses (beans, lentils, peas)
Riboflavin	Meat, milk, cheese, eggs, fish, pulses (beans, lentils, peas), fortified breakfast cereals
Niacin	Meat, liver, fish, nuts, wholegrain cereals, milk, cheese, eggs
Vitamin B6	Meat, milk, wholegrain cereals, potatoes, pulses (beans, lentils, peas), eggs, vegetables
Vitamin B12	Meat, fish, eggs, milk, cheese
Folic Acid	Liver, dark green leafy vegetables, Marmite, wholegrain cereals, oranges
Pantothenic Acid	Liver, kidney, eggs, vegetables, wholegrain cereals, pulses
Biotin	Liver, kidney, egg yolk, milk, wholegain cereals
Vitamin C	Fruit and vegetables, citrus fruit and fruit juice, berries (such as blackberries, raspberries and blackcurrants), dark green vegetables and potatoes
Vitamin D	Oily fish, margarine (added during manufacturing), butter, eggs, fortified breakfast cereals

Vitamin E	Vegetable oils, wheatgerm, dark green leafy vegetables, eggs, wholegrain cereals
Vitamin K	Green leafy vegetables especially cabbage, sprouts, cauliflower and spinach.

Minerals

Calcium	Milk, cheese, yogurt, bread, green vegetables, tinned fish (with small bones) such as sardines
Iron	Red meat, liver, wholegrain bread and cereals, pulses, dark green vegetables
Magnesium	Bread, cereals, potatoes, milk, vegetables
Sodium chloride	Salt, processed meats and tinned vegetables, ready-made sauces, pickles, bread, cereal products.
Potassium	Fruit, vegetables, wholegrain cereals
Zinc	Meat, bread, wholegrain cereals, milk, cheese
Copper	Wholegrain cereals, meat, vegetables
Selenium	Vegetables, cereals, meat, eggs, milk
Iodine	Meat, milk, eggs, fish

List of Some Common Foods and the Nutrients in Them

Food	Nutrients
Wholemeal bread	Complex carbohydrate, B vitamins, fibre, iron, zinc, magnesium, vitamin E
White bread	Complex carbohydrate, most of the B vitamins and iron are removed but the flour is then fortified with thiamin, niacin, iron and calcium. Less than half the fibre of wholemeal
Brown rice	Complex carbohydrate, niacin, fibre
White rice	Complex carbohydrate
Whole milk	Protein, fat, calcium, riboflavin, vitamin B12, vitamin A, zinc
Skimmed milk	Protein, calcium, riboflavin, vitamin B12, zinc
Cheese	Protein, fat, calcium, riboflavin, vitamin B12, vitamin A, zinc, sodium
Chicken (grilled)	Protein, riboflavin, niacin, thiamin, iron, zinc
Kentucky fried chicken	Fat, protein, riboflavin, niacin, thiamin, iron, zinc
Baked potato	Complex carbohydrate, protein, fibre, B vitamins, vitamin C
Chips	Fat, complex carbohydrate, fibre, smaller amounts of B vitamins and vitamin C
Crisps	Complex carbohydrate, fat, small amounts of fibre and vitamin C
Beefburger	Protein, fat, B vitamins, iron, zinc
Sausage	Protein, fat, B vitamins, iron, zinc
Biscuits	Complex carbohydrate, fat, sugar
Cake	Complex carbohydrate, fat, sugar

Ice cream	Sugar, fat, small amounts of protein, and calcium
Mars bar	Sugar, fat, small amounts of protein and calcium
Bananas	Fruit sugar, fibre, protein, vitamin B6, folic acid, potassium
Oranges	Fruit sugar, fibre, vitamin C, folic acid, potassium
Spinach	Vitamins A, B6, C, E, riboflavin, calcium, folic acid, iron, magnesium, potassium
Baked beans	Complex carbohydrate, protein, fibre, sugar, iron, zinc, magnesium, thiamin, riboflavin, niacin, B6, sodium
Tinned spaghetti	Complex carbohydrate, sugar, sodium
Wholemeal pasta	Complex carbohydrate, protein, fibre, thiamin, niacin, B6, iron, vitamin E, zinc, magnesium

Healthy and Unhealthy Snacks

DON'T	DO
Chocolate bar	Cereal bars (check label for fat and sugar content – some can be quite high)
Cakes	Sandwiches or rolls with low fat fillings
Danish pastries	Wholewheat scone
Doughnuts	Flapjack
Crisps and similar snacks	Jacket crisps; wholewheat crisps; low-fat crisps
Hamburger	Bap with cheese or salad
Sweets	Sticks of raw vegetables, fresh fruit, unsalted nuts, dried fruit
Cola and other fizzy soft drinks	High juice fruit squash (look for those with no artificial additives), low-sugar Ribena, fruit juice, low fat milk
Ordinary milkshakes	Homemade milkshakes with low-fat milk, fruit and fruit juice
Biscuits	Rice cakes, oatcakes, Wholemeal digestives, bran biscuits, crackers
Chips	Low fat yogurt, fromage frais
Sausage rolls; pasties	Mini pittas with low fat fillings

Shopping Lists

The following lists include a good selection of healthy foods and snacks suitable for children of various ages. There is, of course, considerable overlap as many of the foods form an important part of all children's diets.

● **FOR A THREE-YEAR-OLD**

Cereals:
> Wholemeal and white bread
> Hot oat cereal
> Other breakfast cereal, e.g. Weetabix
> Brown and white rice
> Plain crackers or rice cakes

Fruit and Vegetables:
Buy those in season. Try to introduce your child to as many new varieties as possible.

> *For example:*

Apples	Carrots
Bananas	Potatoes
Satsumas	Frozen peas
Mango	Frozen mixed veg (for stand-by)
Grapes	Swede
Melon	Turnip
Nectarines	Broccoli
Plums	Aubergine

Milk and Dairy Products:
> Whole milk*
> Plain and low-fat fruit yogurt
> Fromage frais
> Cheese

cont'd

For a Three-year-old (cont'd)

Meat, fish, poultry:
>   Frozen or chilled fish, e.g. plaice, cod
>   Chicken or turkey breast
>   Lean cut of lamb or beef

Tinned foods:
>   Low sugar baked beans
>   Fruit canned in juice (e.g. apricots, pineapple)
>   Wholewheat spaghetti

Other Tasty Foods:
>   Eggs
>   Polyunsaturated margarine or butter
>   Marmite
>   Fruit juice
>   Pure fruit spread
>   Smooth peanut butter★★

● **FOR A SEVEN-YEAR-OLD**

By now your child probably eats a wider range of foods. He or she can probably tolerate more fibre in his or her diet so experiment with wholemeal varieties of pasta and different breads. Introduce more pulses (beans, lentils and peas) and new varieties of fruits and vegetables.

Cereals:
>   Wholemeal and brown bread and rolls
>   Breakfast cereal, e.g. Weetabix; Shreddies; Wheat Flakes
>   Brown and white rice
>   Plain crackers or rice cakes
>   Wholemeal and white pasta shapes
>   Wholemeal flour

Fruit and Vegetables:
Buy those in season. Keep introducing your child to as many new varieties as possible. In addition to the list above, try:

Kiwi fruit	Peppers
Apricots	Spring onions and onions

cont'd

For a Seven-year-old (cont'd)

Pineapple	Sweet potatoes
Paw paw	Okra
Watermelon	Courgettes
Grapefruit	Salad vegetables –
Strawberries	lettuce, cress, watercress

Milk and Dairy Products:

Milk – semi-skimmed or whole
Plain and low fat fruit yogurt
Fromage frais
Cheese
Cottage cheese

Meat, fish, poultry:

Frozen or chilled fish, e.g. plaice, cod
Chicken or turkey breast
Lean cut of lamb or beef
Chicken nuggets

Tinned foods:

Tuna in brine or water
Low sugar baked beans
Fruit canned in juice (e.g. apricots, pineapple)
Wholewheat spaghetti

Other Tasty Foods:

Eggs
Polyunsaturated margarine or butter
Marmite
Pure fruit spread
Pizza (preferably wholemeal)
Fruit juice
Nuts**
Peanut butter

● **FOR AN ELEVEN-YEAR-OLD**

By now your child should be eating a wide range of foods. However, he or she will probably be demanding more snacks and 'convenience' or 'junk' foods. In addition to the list above you could add:

 Cereal bars (check fat and sugar content), e.g. Tracker bars
 Frozen jacket wedges
 Low fat sausages and burgers (100% beef)
 Vegetable and soya burgers
 Wholewheat crisps and low fat crisps
 Unsalted nuts and raisins
 Dried fruit e.g. dried apricots, dates, raisins
 Wholemeal scones or crumpets

● **FOR A FIFTEEN-YEAR-OLD**

The shopping list for the 11 year-old-should provide most of what a teenager needs, although you will have noticed the extra quantities by now! Chances are his or her tastes are a little more adventurous. You can try making more unusual dishes or with a little extra spice. Some ingredients you may find useful are:

 Muesli
 Tinned or dried beans – red kidney; borlotti; flageolet; chick peas; etc. Lentils
 Spices – curry powder; coriander; cumin; turmeric; ginger; garam masala. Garlic
 Hummus (chick pea purée) – useful for sandwiches and quick lunches accompanied by pitta bread and salad
 Vegetable and stock concentrates – for soups, casseroles, stews
 Fresh or frozen seafood such as prawns and cockles

* Children under five should be given whole milk (full-fat milk) although semi-skimmed may be introduced after the age of two. This is because of the low energy (calorie) and vitamin A content of skimmed milk.

** Whole nuts should not be given to children under five because of the risk of choking. Smooth peanut butter is fine.

Where to Buy Fruit and Vegetables

Most supermarkets have high standards when it comes to selecting fresh foods and they have a fast turnover. Whether you prefer to shop at a large supermarket or smaller grocer, look carefully at the fruit and vegetables and, if you can, feel as well to make sure they are firm and not wilted, wrinkled, over-ripe, damaged, or soft and squashy. You can usually guarantee market stalls will have the freshest (and cheapest) produce but still check for damaged or sub-standard specimens. Greengrocers and large supermarkets are also a fairly good bet.

If you can't always get fresh fruit and vegetables, or you are in a hurry, frozen is a good alternative. Nutritionally there is often little difference between fresh and frozen (especially if the so-called 'fresh' vegetable has been stored for several days before eating). Most frozen vegetables have been frozen within a couple of hours of being picked so there is little time for vitamin loss to occur. The main drawback with them is their loss of flavour and change in texture as a result of the freezing process. Keep a packet or two handy for emergencies but try to buy fresh wherever possible.

It is a different story with tinned fruit and vegetables. The canning process causes far more destruction of vitamins than freezing. Most vegetables are canned in brine so can be quite salty. Buy fruit fresh whenever you can but if you want to have a can handy for the store cupboard, go for the varieties canned in fruit juice rather than syrup.

Healthy Menus for Children

● FOR A THREE-YEAR-OLD

Breakfast

    Instant hot oat cereal made with milk

    Fingers ('soldiers') of wholemeal toast and Marmite

    1 boiled egg

Lunch

    Baked beans on wholemeal toast with a little grated cheese

    Low fat yogurt

    Chopped apple

    Cup of milk

Tea

    Grilled homemade fish cakes

    Pieces of jacket potato or jacket wedges

    Peas and carrots

    Cup of milk

    Satsuma or other fresh fruit

● FOR A SEVEN-YEAR-OLD

Breakfast

    1 bowl Shreddies or other wholewheat cereal with milk and a chopped banana

    Wholemeal toast and pure fruit spread

    Glass of milk

Lunch

    Cheese and tomato pizza (preferably wholemeal)

    Slices of cucumber or baked beans

    Low fat yogurt

Tea

    Wholemeal sandwich squares filled with tuna and tomato

    OR chicken and salad   *cont'd*

For a Seven-year-old (cont'd)

Supper
>   Baked chicken nuggets
>   Boiled or mashed potato (with milk)
>   Peas and sweetcorn
>   Banana (or other fruit) with custard

● **FOR AN ELEVEN-YEAR-OLD**

Breakfast
>   Orange juice
>   Weetabix with milk
>   Wholemeal toast with pure fruit spread
>   Glass of milk

Lunch
>   Jacket potato topped with tuna or cheese and sweetcorn
>   Mixed vegetables
>   Banana

Tea
>   Wholemeal roll filled with cooked chicken or cottage cheese
>   and tomato
>   Glass of milk

Supper
>   Macaroni cheese
>   Vegetables
>   Fresh fruit

● **FOR A FIFTEEN-YEAR-OLD**

Breakfast
>   Muesli with milk or yogurt
>   Fresh fruit

Lunch
>   Homemade beefburger in a wholemeal bap
>   Salad
>   Low fat yogurt
>   Fresh fruit

Tea
>   Wholemeal sandwich filled with cheese or tuna and salad
>   Glass of milk

Supper
>   Vegetable soup
>   Chilli con carne with brown rice or beef and vegetable curry
>   with brown rice
>   Fruit salad with yogurt or fromage frais

Diet Suggestions for Mothers-to-be

(Quantities will depend on individual calorie needs)

MENU 1

Breakfast
>   1 glass pure orange juice
>   1 bowl bran flakes with 1 chopped banana and ⅓ pint
>   low-fat milk
>   Wholewheat toast and pure fruit spread

Mid-morning
>   1 glass low-fat milk or 1 carton low fat yogurt

cont'd

Diet Suggestions for Mothers-to-be (cont'd)

Mid-day
>   Wholewheat sandwich filled with tuna or chicken or low-fat cheese and salad
>   Fresh fruit

Mid-afternoon
>   As mid-morning

Evening meal
>   Grilled or baked fish
>   Large helping of vegetables or salad
>   Brown rice
>   Fruit salad with plain yogurt

MENU 2

Breakfast
>   Grapefruit or other fresh fruit
>   Boiled egg
>   Wholewheat toast

Mid-morning
>   Glass of low-fat milk or low-fat yogurt

Mid-day
>   Jacket potato with cottage cheese, tuna or baked beans
>   Salad
>   Low-fat fromage frais or yogurt

Mid-afternoon
>   Fresh fruit

Evening meal
>   Clear vegetable soup
>   Chicken and vegetable casserole or chicken and vegetable stir-fry
>   Wholewheat pasta or rice
>   Side salad
>   Baked apples with plain yogurt or fromage frais

Vitamin and Mineral Content of Some Leading Brands of Baby Formula Milks

[per 100 millilitres as fed]

		Human Breast Milk	Farley's Ostermilk	Farley's Ostermilk 2
Vitamin A	(mcg)	60	97	100
Thiamin (B1)	(mcg)	16	42	39
Riboflavin (B2)	(mcg)	31	55	53
Vitamin B6	(mcg)	5.9	35	33
Vitamin B12	(mcg)	0.01	0.14	0.13
Biotin	(mcg)	0.76	1	0.97
Folic Acid	(mcg)	5.2	3.4	3.2
Niacin	(mcg)	230	690	650
Pantothenic Acid	(mcg)	260	230	220
Vitamin C	(mg)	3.8	6.9	6.4
Vitamin D	(mcg)	–	1	1
Vitamin E	(mg)	0.35	0.48	0.48
Vitamin K	(mcg)	2.7	2.6	7
Calcium	(mg)	35	35	61
Chloride	(mg)	43	45	56
Copper	(mcg)	39	42	39
Iodine	(mcg)	7	4.5	10
Iron	(mcg)	76	650	650
Magnesium	(mg)	2.8	5.2	6
Manganese	(mcg)	–	3.4	3.3
Phosphorus	(mg)	15	29	49
Potassium	(mg)	60	57	86
Sodium	(mg)	15	19	25
Zinc	(mcg)	295	340	330

Farley's OsterPrem*	Cow & Gate Premium	Cow & Gate Plus	Cow & Gate Soya Formula	Aptamil
100	60	80	80	60.5
95	40	40	40	40.3
180	100	100	100	50.7
100	40	40	40	30.3
0.2	0.2	0.2	0.2	0.16
2	1.5	1.5	1.5	1.1
50	10	10	10	10.1
1000	400	400	400	400
500	300	300	300	400
28	8	8	8	6
8	1.1	1.1	1.1	1
10	1.1	1.1	1.3	0.7
–	5	5	5	4
70	54	85	54	59.2
60	40	60	40	37.7
120	40	40	40	46
7	7	7	13	4
40	500	500	40	700
5	5	7	5	6.5
3	7	7	33	4.2
35	27	55	27	35.1
65	65	100	65	84.5
45	18	25	18	18.2
1000	400	400	400	400

* suitable only for premature babies

cont'd

Vitamin and Mineral Content of Some Leading Brands of Baby Formula Milks (cont'd)

		Human Breast Milk	Milumil	Prematil*
Vitamin A	(mcg)	60	57	63
Thiamin (B1)	(mcg)	16	32	40
Riboflavin (B2)	(mcg)	31	49	140
Vitamin B6	(mcg)	5.9	42	90
Vitamin B12	(mcg)	0.01	0.2	0.15
Biotin	(mcg)	0.76	1.1	1.1
Folic Acid	(mcg)	5.2	.5	43
Niacin	(mcg)	230	240	600
Pantothenic Acid	(mcg)	260	240	300
Vitamin C	(mg)	3.8	7.6	15
Vitamin D	(mcg)	–	1	2.1
Vitamin E	(mg)	0.35	0.8	2
Vitamin K	(mg)	2.7	4	2.8
Calcium	(mg)	35	71	70
Chloride	(mg)	43	44	40
Copper	(mcg)	39	27	64
Iodine	(mcg)	7	2	10
Iron	(mcg)	76	430	100
Magnesium	(mg)	2.8	6	6
Manganese	(mcg)	–	13	20
Phosphorus	(mg)	15	55	35
Potassium	(mg)	60	85	75
Sodium	(mg)	15	24	30
Zinc	(mcg)	295	410	392

* suitable only for premature babies

SMA Gold	SMA White	Progress	Wysoy
79	79	69	60
67	67	81	67
100	100	120	100
42	42	48	42
0.13	0.13	0.12	0.2
1.5	1.5	1.71	3.5
5	5	6	5
500	500	610	500
210	210	240	300
5.5	5.5	6.6	5.5
1	1	1.2	1
0.64	0.64	0.73	0.64
	5.5	5.5	10 6.6
42	46	115	40
40	42	75	40
47	47	58	47
6	3.4	6.9	6
670	670	120	670
4.5	4	9.4	6.7
15	15	17	20
28	36	94	42
56	62	105	70
15	18	35	18
500	500	430	500

What to Look for in Multi-Vitamin and Mineral Supplements

Not all supplements are the same. Some manufacturers include widely differing amounts of nutrients in their formulas, and as a result there are quite a few multi-supplements on the market in Britain that are almost worthless.

It is important that you and your children get the full spectrum of all the essential minerals and vitamins, preferably every day.

Fortunately, the manufacturers are required by law to list the exact ingredients of their supplements, so it is a relatively simple matter for you to check the small print on the side of the bottle or packet, and scrutinise exactly what's inside.

I have listed below the ideal average daily intakes of the major vitamins and minerals for children, adults, and pregnant and nursing mothers. The figures are based on the Recommended Daily Amounts in the United States. Because people differ in their nutritional needs, these figures are not gospel; some people may need less, others may need more. However, they are a good guide to the sort of intake you should be aiming at.

Take this book with you, and go round your local supermarkets, chemists and health food stores indentifying the best brands by their list of ingredients. You may not find many on sale in Britain that reach the ideal levels, but go for those which get closest to them in terms of the range and quantity of nutrients.

The quantity of ingredients will be listed as either:

mg = milligrams   or
mcg or ug = micrograms   or
I.U. = International Units   (rarely)

It's worth trying more than one brand of supplement as they differ in their palatability, especially to children. Some people don't like the taste of uncoated pills, others find some pills 'repeat' on them. Experiment until you find brands you and your children are happy with.

Pregnant and breastfeeding mothers should also be aware they have extra nutritional requirements.

Vitamin and Mineral Checklist: 1989 Recommended Dietary Allowances

The following seven tables are based on 1989 RDA (see page 158).

Children aged 1–3

Vitamin A	400 mcg	Potassium	1000 mg
Vitamin D	10 mcg	Calcium	800 mg
Vitamin E	6 mg	Phosphorus	800 mg
Vitamin K	15 mcg	Magnesium	80 mg
Thiamin (B1)	0.7 mg	Iron	10 mg
Riboflavin (B2)	0.8 mg	Iodine	70 mcg
Niacin (B3)	9 mg	Fluoride	1 mg
Pantothenic acid (B5)	3 mg	Zinc	10 mg
Pyridoxine (B6)	1 mg	Copper	0.8 mg
Biotin (B8)	20 mcg	Chromium	50 mcg
Folic acid	50 mcg	Manganese	1.2 mg
Vitamin B12	0.7 mcg	Selenium	20 mcg
Vitamin C	40 mg	Molybdenum	40 mcg

★ Best all-round supplement brand: 'Minamino'

Children aged 4–6

Vitamin A	500 mcg	Potassium	1400 mg
Vitamin D	10 mcg	Calcium	800 mg
Vitamin E	7 mg	Phosphorus	800 mg
Vitamin K	20 mcg	Magnesium	120 mg
Thiamin (B1)	0.9 mg	Iron	10 mg
Riboflavin (B2)	1.1 mg	Iodine	90 mcg
Niacin (B3)	12 mg	Fluoride	1.75 mg
Pantothenic acid (B5)	3.5 mg	Zinc	10 mg
Pyridoxine (B6)	1.1 mg	Copper	1.25 mg
Biotin (B8)	25 mcg	Chromium	90 mcg
Folic acid	75 mcg	Manganese	1.75 mg
Vitamin B12	1 mcg	Selenium	20 mcg
Vitamin C	45 mg	Molybdenum	50 mcg

★ Best all-round supplement brands: Nature's Best 'Children's Chews', 'Forceval Junior', 'Superted Vitamins with Iron'

Vitamin and Mineral Checklist (cont'd)

Children aged 7–10

Vitamin A	700 mcg	Potassium	1600 mg
Vitamin D	10 mcg	Calcium	800 mg
Vitamin E	7 mg	Phosphorus	800 mg
Vitamin K	30 mcg	Magnesium	170 mg
Thiamin (B1)	1 mg	Iron	10 mg
Riboflavin (B2)	1.2 mg	Iodine	120 mcg
Niacin (B3)	13 mg	Fluoride	2 mg
Pantothenic acid (B5)	4.5 mg	Zinc	10 mg
Pyridoxine (B6)	1.4 mg	Copper	1.5 mg
Biotin (B8)	30 mcg	Chromium	125 mcg
Folic acid	100 mcg	Manganese	2.5 mg
Vitamin B12	1.4 mcg	Selenium	30 mcg
Vitamin C	45 mg	Molybdenum	100 mcg

★ Best all-round supplement brands: Healthcrafts 'Junior Vitachieve'

Children aged 11–14

Vitamin A	1000 mcg	Potassium	200 mg
Vitamin D	10 mcg	Calcium	1200 mg
Vitamin E	10 mg	Phosphorus	1200 mg
Vitamin K	45 mcg	Magnesium	270 mg
Thiamin (B1)	1.3 mg	Iron	12 mg
Riboflavin (B2)	1.5 mg	Iodine	150 mcg
Niacin (B3)	17 mg	Fluoride	2 mg
Pantothenic acid (B5)	5.5 mg	Zinc	15 mg
Pyridoxine (B6)	1.7 mg	Copper	2 mg
Biotin (B8)	76 mcg	Chromium	125 mcg
Folic acid	150 mcg	Manganese	3.5 mg
Vitamin B12	2 mcg	Selenium	40 mcg
Vitamin C	50 mg	Molybdenum	150 mcg

(Recommended daily intakes for girls is slightly less than above.)
★ Best all-round supplement brands: Healthcrafts 'Vitachieve', Seven Seas 'Multivitamins and Minerals', 'Tandem IQ', Vital Life 'Multi-Vitamin/Mineral'

Vitamin and Mineral Checklist (cont'd)
Children aged 15–18

Vitamin A	1000 mcg	Potassium	2000 mg
Vitamin D	10 mcg	Calcium	1200 mg
Vitamin E	10 mg	Phosphorus	1200 mg
Vitamin K	65 mcg	Magnesium	400 mg
Thiamin (B1)	1.5 mg	Iron	12 mg
Riboflavin (B2)	1.8 mg	Iodine	150 mcg
Niacin (B3)	20 mg	Fluoride	2 mg
Pantothenic acid (B5)	5.5 mg	Zinc	15 mg
Pyridoxine (B6)	2 mg	Copper	2.5 mg
Biotin (B8)	70 mcg	Chromium	125 mcg
Folic acid	200 mcg	Manganese	3.5 mg
Vitamin B12	2 mcg	Selenium	50 mcg
Vitamin C	60 mg	Molybdenum	150 mcg

(Recommended daily intake for girls is slightly less than above.)
★ Best all-round supplement brands: Healthcrafts 'Vitachieve', Seven Seas 'Multivitamins and Minerals', 'Tandem IQ', Vital Life 'Multivitamin/Mineral'

Pregnant women

Vitamin A	800 mcg	Potassium	2000 mg
Vitamin D	10 mcg	Calcium	1200 mg
Vitamin E	10 mg	Phosphorus	1200 mg
Vitamin K	65 mcg	Magnesium	320 mg
Thiamin (B1)	1.5 mg	Iron	30 mg
Riboflavin (B2)	1.6 mg	Iodine	175 mcg
Niacin (B3)	17 mg	Fluoride	2.5 mg
Pantothenic acid (B5)	5.5 mg	Zinc	15 mg
Pyridoxine (B6)	2.2 mg	Copper	2.5 mg
Biotin (B8)	70 mcg	Chromium	125 mcg
Folic acid	400 mcg	Manganese	3.5 mg
Vitamin B12	2.2 mcg	Selenium	65 mcg
Vitamin C	70 mg	Molybdenum	150 mcg

★ Best all-round supplement brands: Healthcrafts 'Vitachieve', Seven Seas 'Multivitamins and Minerals'

Vitamin and Mineral Checklist (cont'd)
Breastfeeding women

Vitamin A	1300 mcg	Potassium	2000 mg
Vitamin D	10 mcg	Calcium	1200 mg
Vitamin E	12 mg	Phosphorus	1200 mg
Vitamin K	65 mcg	Magnesium	355 mg
Thiamin (B1)	1.5 mg	Iron	15 mg
Riboflavin (B2)	1.8 mg	Iodine	200 mcg
Niacin (B3)	20 mg	Fluoride	2.5 mg
Pantothenic acid (B5)	5.5 mg	Zinc	19 mg
Pyridoxine (B6)	2.1 mg	Copper	2.5 mg
Biotin (B8)	70 mcg	Chromium	125 mcg
Folic acid	280 mcg	Manganese	3.5 mg
Vitamin B12	2.6 mcg	Selenium	75 mcg
Vitamin C	95 mg	Molybdenum	150 mcg

★ Best all-round supplement brands: Healthcrafts 'Vitachieve', Seven Seas 'Multivitamins and Minerals'

Toxic Doses of Vitamins

All vitamins are of course safe at the RDA level. In fact, for most there is a considerable margin of safety above the RDA levels, before any vitamin causes adverse reactions. Pregnant women should avoid taking any more than 2000 micrograms of Vitamin A per day. Adverse reactions are rare, and when they are noticed, they can be readily cleared up by ceasing to take the vitamin, with no long-term effects.

In ascending order of safety . . .

Vitamin A	is safe up to	3 times the RDA
Vitamin D	,,	5 ,,
Vitamin K	,,	20 ,,
Thiamin	,,	50 ,,
Pyridoxine	,,	50 ,,
Niacin	,,	50 ,,
Riboflavin	,,	100 ,,
Pantothenic acid	,,	100 ,,
Folic acid	,,	100 ,,
Biotin	,,	100 ,,
Vitamin B12	,,	100 ,,
Vitamin C	,,	100 ,,
Vitamin E	,,	100 ,,

from Marks, J., *The Vitamins, their role in medical practice*, MTP Press, 1985.

Minerals

You should not exceed three times the Recommended Daily intake of any mineral.

Publications by the Author

'The Effects of Sugar on the Treatment and Control of Antisocial Behavior on an Incarcerated Juvenile Population', *The International Journal of Biosocial Research* 3(1): 1–9; 1982

'Diet and Crime: An Empirical Examination of the Value of Nutrition in the Control and Treatment of Incarcerated Juvenile Offenders', *The International Journal of Biosocial Research* 4(1): 25–39; 1983

With Walter E. Doraz, Ph D, 'Types of Offenses which can be Reduced in an Institutional Setting Using Nutritional Intervention: A Preliminary Empirical Evaluation', *The International Journal of Biosocial Research* 4(2): 74–84; 1983

'Diet and Delinquency. A Multi-State Replication', *The International Journal of Biosocial Research* 5(2): 70–78; 1983

'The Alabama Diet-Behavior Program: An Evaluation at the Coosa Valley Regional Detention Center', *The International Journal of Biosocial Research* 5(2): 79–87; 1983

'The Los Angeles Probation Department Diet-Behavior Program: An Empirical Analysis of Six Institutional Settings' *The International Journal of Biosocial Research* 5(2): 88–98; 1983

'The Northern California Diet-Behavior Program: An Empirical Evaluation of 3000 Incarcerated Juveniles in Stanislaus County Juvenile Hall', *The International Journal of Biosocial Research* 5(2): 99–106; 1983

'The Effects of Citrus on the Treatment and Control of Antisocial Behavior: A Double-Blind Crossover Study of an Incarcerated

Juvenile Population', *The International Journal of Biosocial Research* 5(2): 107–117; 1983

'Institutional Nutritional Policies and Criminal Behavior', *Nutrition Today* 20(3): 16–25; 1985

'Diet and Delinquency: Empirical Testing of Seven Theories', *The International Journal of Biosocial Research* 7(2): 108–131; 1986

With Walter E. Doraz Ph D and James Wakefield Jr Ph D, 'The Impact of a Low Food Additive and Sucrose Diet on Academic Performance in 803 New York City Public Schools', *The International Journal of Biosocial Research* 8(2): 185–195; 1986

With Walter E. Doraz Ph D and James Wakefield Jr Ph D, 'The Testing of Various Hypotheses as Explanations for the Gains in National Standardized Academic Test Scores in the 1978–1983 New York City Nutrition Policy Modification Project', *The International Journal of Biosocial Research* 8(2): 196–203; 1986

'Malnutrition and Maladaptive Behavior' in W. Essman (ed.), *Nutrition and Brain Function* (Basel, Karger Press, 1987) pp. 198–217

'Diet and Criminal Behavior: A Criminological Evaluation of the Arlington, Virginia Proceedings', *The International Journal of Biosocial Research* 9(2): 1–20; 1987

With Stephen P. Amos MA, Walter E. Doraz Ph D, Mary Ann Kelly RD, Justine Pinto MA and James Wakefield Jr Ph D, 'Controlled Trial of Vitamin-Mineral Supplementation on Intelligence and Brain Function' (Unpublished on going to press)

With Stephen P. Amos MA, Walter E. Doraz Ph D, Mary Ann Kelly RD, George D. Muedeking Ph D, Justine Pinto MA and James Wakefield Jr Ph D, 'Controlled Trial of Vitamin-Mineral Supplementation on Institutional Violence and Antisocial Behavior (Unpublished on going to press)

Index